The Watermills of Surrey 1990
has been published in a
Limited Edition
of which this is

Number 128

A list of subscribers
is printed at the
back of the book

The WATERMILLS of SURREY

FRONT COVER: Rickford Mill at work in 1941. (RCHME)

Milton Court Mill near to collapse in the 1860s. (DK)

The WATERMILLS of SURREY

BY

DEREK STIDDER

BARRACUDA BOOKS LIMITED
BUCKINGHAM, ENGLAND
MCMCX

PUBLISHED BY BARRACUDA BOOKS LIMITED
BUCKINGHAM, ENGLAND
AND PRINTED BY
NUFFIELD PRESS
COWLEY, OXFORD

BOUND BY
WBC BOOKBINDERS LIMITED
MAESTEG, WALES

JACKET PRINTED BY
CHENEY & SONS LIMITED
BANBURY, OXON

LITHOGRAPHY BY
BANBURY BOOKS AND JOURNALS
BANBURY, OXON

TYPESET BY
HARPER PHOTOTYPESETTERS LIMITED
NORTHAMPTON, ENGLAND

© Derek Stidder 1990

ISBN 0 86023 480 0

CONTENTS

A CKNOWLEDGEMENTS

This book would not have been possible without the assistance of many people and organisations who have patiently provided me with information, or have pointed out the existence of further research material. In particular, I am grateful to Alan Crocker and Colin Smith for their help and encouragement. Also, specific thanks are given to the mill owners who, without exception, have let me roam freely about their property to measure, record and photograph as I required. Photography has played an important part in this book, and I would like to thank Nick Catford and Chris Shepheard for their assistance in the reproduction of photographs.

The staff or members of the following organisations have kindly assisted me with my research; Guildford Muniment Room; the Surrey Archaeological Society Library; the Surrey Record Office; the British Museum, for permission to consult the Simmons papers for Surrey, held in their archive collection; Weybridge Museum; Chertsey Museum; Kingston Museum and Heritage Centre; Farnham Museum; the Surrey Industrial History Group and the Wind and Watermill Section of the SPAB.

Finally, I would especially like to thank Mr R. Hawksley for his constructive criticism of my manuscript, and furthermore, for providing additional research information.

Jack Hillier's book, *Old Surrey Watermills*, published in 1951, provided the inspiration for me to explore the subject in depth. Surrey is a poor county in terms of extant watermills when compared to its neighbours Kent, Sussex and Hampshire and, therefore, I felt it was important that the history of Surrey's watermills should be recorded. In recent years, a large amount of research material has become available for public inspection and, in this respect, I have been most fortunate.

In the forty years since the publication of Jack Hillier's book, several watermills have become derelict or have been demolished, and without doubt this will unfortunately continue in future years. Some organisations, like the Wind and Watermill Section of the SPAB attempt, on a national scale, to rectify the situation but even they are seemingly powerless to restrict or amend the proposals of the property developer.

This book is specifically about the history of watermills in Surrey. Detailed machinery operation, and general watermill history, have been kept to a minimum, as several excellent books already exist on these subjects. However, I have found it impossible to investigate the history of every site within the county, as information concerning some is extremely scarce. I have concentrated mainly on the principal industry of flour milling, and also special attention has been given to the 47 sites where mill buildings remain although, of these, just eight mills are complete with machinery, with one capable of working using traditional methods.

Unfortunately, of the remaining 64 mills, most have long disappeared, and in many cases, nothing tangible remains to even indicate the position of a former watermill site.

FOREWORD

*by Professor A. G. Crocker FSA DSc CEng, Chairman, Surrey Industrial History Group;
Past-Chairman, Wind and Watermill Section, SPAB*

I first met Derek Stidder in 1974, when he contributed to a series of adult education lectures on industrial archaeology which I helped to organise at the University of Surrey. His topic was, of course, 'The Watermills of Surrey' and the knowledge and enthusiasm which he and his fellow lecturers exhibited led to the formation of the Surrey Industrial History Group. Derek became a key committee member and produced the Group's first local guide on 'The Industrial Archaeology of Reigate and Banstead District'. He also introduced my wife and me to the Wind and Watermill Section of the Society for the Protection of Ancient Buildings. This has resulted in us becoming deeply involved in the study of mills nationally, although our interests have concentrated mainly on paper mills and gunpowder mills rather than the more familiar corn mills.

Over the years Derek Stidder has accumulated a wealth of information on the watermills of Surrey. He has always been willing to share this information with colleagues and to help with their documentary research and recording. In particular he has produced several detailed surveys of Surrey mills which SIHG proposed to restore but unfortunately the owners could not be persuaded of the importance of these projects. We have also, for example, squelched in the mud beneath Oxted Mill, recording a rare Gunther 'Girard' water turbine and marvelled at the magnificent but unusual timber gearing which we recorded at Farnham High Mill.

In this book Derek Stidder has presented us with a fascinating selection of information from his collection of material on the mills of Surrey. All those who appreciate the traditional qualities of mill buildings, their equipment and the people associated with them will be grateful to him for carrying out the dedicated research which has made this possible. It will surely encourage us all to take a greater interest in the mills in our localities and perhaps even convince some mill owners that restoration projects are worthwhile after all!

Alan Crocker

DEDICATION

For Moira

PREFACE

by David Shepherd OBE FRSA

So much of our industrial heritage has been swept aside in my lifetime in the name of progress — that awesome word that seems to justify the destruction of so much of our past because nobody cared or the demands of 'development' were paramount.

I therefore believe that a book such as this fulfils a useful purpose. It helps to awaken interest in our past history which in turn must surely improve the quality of life of those young people growing up in the otherwise seemingly so functional age in which we live.

I was particularly delighted when asked to write this preface and perhaps it is not entirely inappropriate as there is a beautiful but somewhat neglected watermill just a few hundred yards away from where I write, in my own village of Hascombe. I wish this book all the success it deserves.

David Shepherd

KEY TO CAPTION CREDITS

BHM	Bourne Hall Museum
CM	Chertsey Museum
CS	Colin Smith
DK	Dave Knight
DN	Donald Neville
FF	Francis Frith Collection
JA	John Axten
JS	John Smith
KMHC	Kingston Museum and Heritage Centre
MM	Michael Manser
MH	Mike Hood
NC	Nick Catford
RP	Roger Packham
RCHM	Royal Commission on the Historic Monuments — England
SPD	Surrey County Council Planning Dept.
SLSL	Surrey Local Studies Library (Guildford)
WM	Weybridge Museum

All other photographs and illustrations are from the author's collection.

INTRODUCTION

Surrey was never an important county in terms of major industrial output and production. There were notable exceptions to this, especially with regard to the Chilworth gunpowder mills which, during the 17th and 18th centuries, were the most important in the country. To a lesser extent, there was also the involvement with the Wealden iron industry in the southern and south-eastern part of the county.

Just over a century ago, the boundary of Surrey to the north was the River Thames from Putney to Deptford. When an Act of Parliament of 1888 transferred nearly 26,000 acres of north Surrey to London, the county, to a certain extent, lost its direct trade outlet through the Port of London. As if the 1888 Act were not enough, in 1965 London again took another slice of the county for its administrative use and important Surrey towns, such as Richmond, Kingston, Sutton and Croydon, were duly incorporated as London boroughs. In return for the loss of these historically important towns, the county was given an area of Middlesex in and around the Staines area.

The decision to investigate the history of Surrey's corn mills sites within the present administrative county will cause concern to certain historians, who may well feel that the historical county prior to 1888 should form the study area. The only river affected would be the River Wandle, which rises near Croydon and enters the Thames at Wandsworth. The fall of this river is ideal for watermill use and, in its relatively short length of just over eight miles, at least 43 watermills were working during the latter half of the 19th century. The industrial uses were varied, so the River Wandle has been omitted, as it merits its own study.

In the south-west part of the county, in the Haslemere area, there are several watermill sites 'shared' with Hampshire. In one instance the mill buildings are in Hampshire with the county boundary mered to the bypass channel. These watermill sites have been included. The lower part of the Hogsmill River is technically outside the study area, but the three sites in Kingston have been included for historical reasons. However, the watermill sites in the Staines area have been omitted as they form no part of Surrey's watermill history.

Historically, the majority of the watermill sites were originally developed as corn mills but, over the ensuing centuries, other industrial processes took advantage of the available water power. The most notable was for the production of hand-made paper, with the River Wey and the Tilling Bourne the principal rivers. Gunpowder mills flourished to the south of London, away from the inhabited areas and, apart from the large and well-known mills at Chilworth, other sites at Molesey, Ewell, Godstone, Worcester Park and Abinger supported gunpowder mills at various times. Leather dressing was another industry that took advantage of the available water supply in the south-west with Godalming the main production area. For centuries the manufacture of woollen garments was the principal cottage industry for towns and villages, with Guildford, Godalming and Farnham all becoming wool trade centres. The process of cleaning the natural animal fat from the woollen fibres was carried out using Fuller's Earth, and fortunately one of the few areas in the country where this is deposited is to the east of Redhill, where vast amounts have been removed using open-cast mining techniques. Fulling mills were one of the earliest applications of water power, apart from corn mills, and there is a reference to such a mill at Guildford in 1251. Other smaller and more localised manufacturing processes, such as for brass wire and iron artifacts, existed at various sites around the county, but the lack of natural deposits prevented these from becoming major Surrey industries.

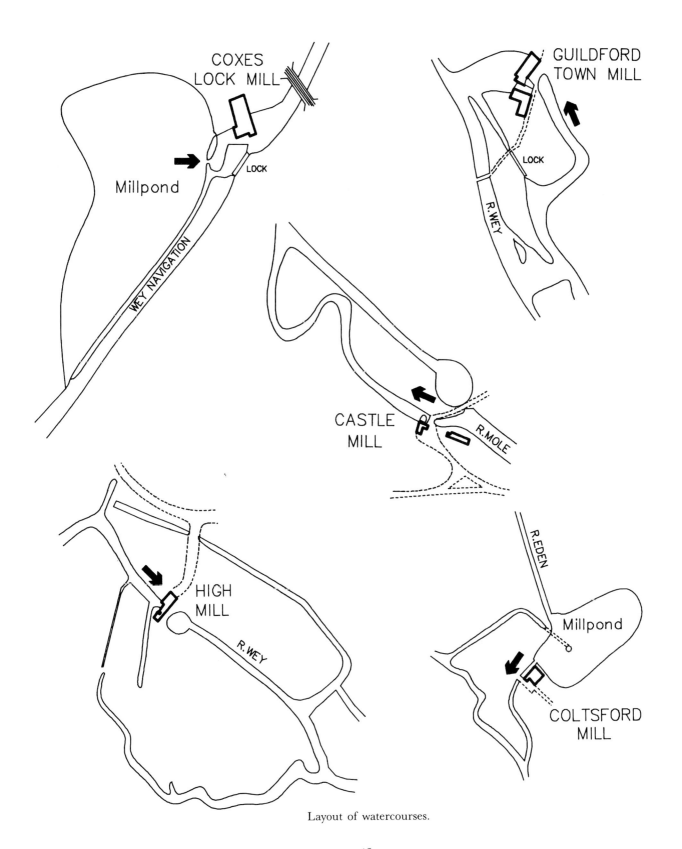

Layout of watercourses.

THE WATERMILL IN SURREY

The breaking of the wheat kernel to produce flour was a common practice thousands of years ago, as it is today, although production processes have altered dramatically over the centuries.

Initially, the reduction was carried out using a saddle or hand quern, but later on animal power was utilized. The Romans instigated the geared watermill, although rivers and streams of Mediterranean countries were not conducive to the economic production of flour in quantities from a single mill. The first type of watermill to use machinery was known as the 'Greek Mill', which consisted of a horizontal vaned waterwheel, the shaft of which was connected directly to a pair of millstones, set above it. The natural development from this basic layout was to employ a vertically mounted waterwheel connected to geared machinery.

Originally watermills were small and only contained one pair of stones, and this layout certainly lasted in many until the last years of the 18th century when social reform demanded greater flour output and soon watermills containing two to five pairs of stones were erected.

After the decline of the Roman Empire, there was little technical advancement until the Saxons started to build watermills. The Domesday Survey of 1086 first documented watermill locations, although this record was not necessarily accurate or comprehensive. The medieval period saw the advent of the manorial mill, the domination of landowners and the introduction of milling soke. This feudal system gave landowners the sole right to erect watermills and to compel their tenants to bring their grain to their mill. The miller would then extract, on behalf of the owner, a toll of flour, normally a sixteenth, by way of payment. This was unpopular; the miller was distrusted and often accused of taking excessive toll.

The church, through the monasteries, was one of the biggest landowners in Surrey with Chertsey Abbey, for instance, controlling vast areas in the north-west of the county. The monasteries erected watermills and many of these sites were used after the Dissolution. After the reign of Elizabeth I, the milling soke system was gradually relaxed, which led in turn to new mills or modernisation. However, the greatest expansion of the industry took place in the first half of the 19th century as the railway spread its tentacles into the south-east. Millers could buy grain and sell flour over a greater area; many mills were extended to increase their storage capacity. At Castle Mill, Dorking, such an enlargement took place, and a piece of paper found after a fire at the mill in 1933, hidden in the flooring, reinforces this view. The note contained the following message:

'I write this note to show the state of things at the time of writing. The railroad is just about to commence and a great deal of work is expected on this account. The enlargement of Castle Mill has been completed for Dr Dewdney, which will be seen by the person finding this note. We work very hard but the drink comes seldom. Mr Dewdney is a rather arbitrary fellow and we can scarce give satisfaction. John Hildeen, Henry Sawyer and William Mays, carpenters.'

With the rapid advances in technical innovation and the continuous improvement in the milling craft, it was inevitable that mechanical engineering techniques would eventually lead to the decline of the watermill, especially so in the more rural areas. The introduction of steam power certainly started the downward trend while the implementation of the roller mill caused a radical change. Henry Simon of Manchester was one of the first companies to erect complete roller milling plants, with four hundred systems installed by them in England and Ireland by 1892.

Another factor for major change was the repeal of the Corn Laws in 1846. This allowed vast quantities of foreign wheat to be imported and large steam mills were set up in and around the Port of London. In the year ending December 1892, for instance, 64,896,799 cwt of foreign wheat was imported, the majority coming from the Atlantic side of the USA (27,018,996 cwt). Rural watermills could not compete with this new and ultimate threat to their economic existence and many mills either closed down or carried on grinding for local use. Watermills on the River Wey Navigation were more fortunate than most, with easy access to and from the Thames and several were converted to roller milling; to some extent they prospered.

As these struggled on, others, mainly in the more rural areas, closed down or continued just to grind animal feed. This was a sad chapter in the history of watermilling as sites closed down in their thousands throughout the country. As steam had replaced water power, so electricity eventually took its place, although the machinery to be found in a modern flour mill bears little resemblance to that in existence one hundred years ago. Coxe's Lock Mill at Addlestone was one Surrey mill that survived commercially, but now even this has been closed down for economic reasons.

The River Wey and the River Mole are the two principal waterways in the county, both of which run in a northerly direction to their confluence with the Thames. Both rivers, in terms of water capacity, so contrast with each other that in the eastern part of the county several tributaries of the River Mole had to be utilised rather than the main river itself.

The River Mole enters the county as a small stream near Gatwick Airport and then meanders across Surrey, bypassing Reigate but passing through Dorking, Leatherhead, Cobham and Esher before entering the Thames at East Molesey. Its upper reaches proved unsuitable for the erection of a mill, owing to the erratic seasonal variation in water level. At Castle Mill, at Dorking there is a mill adjacent to the main river, even though here a weir had to be constructed across the river to regulate the flow of water into the mill race. Downstream from Dorking, the River Mole becomes wider and more purposeful with but one of the eight mill sites off the main river itself — Fetcham Mill, near Leatherhead.

One of the main tributaries of the Mole is the Pippbrook, which issues from the slopes of Leith Hill and then flows in an easterly direction through Dorking. At one time this stream worked seven watermills and one water pumping mill in only a total length of five miles, although each mill site had to have its own water storage facility. Also to be found in the eastern side of the county, near to the boundary with Kent, is a small tributary of the Medway. Notable extant watermills to be found here are Haxted Mill, which is now a watermill museum, and Coltsford Mill, the last working watermill in Surrey, which still uses waterpower and traditional machinery.

Moving westwards across the county is the Tilling Bourne, a tributary of the River Wey, which also issues from the slopes of Leith Hill. This stream was an important waterway for Surrey's industry and, although only nine miles long, supported one of the most important gunpowder mills in the country at Chilworth, as well as paper and iron manufacture, and several corn mills, such as Shalford Mill and Gomshall Mill.

The River Wey can be classified as Surrey's main watermill river, even though much of it lies within Hampshire. The river enters the county at Farnham, and then bisects the important towns of West Surrey, such as Farnham, Godalming, Guildford, Woking and Weybridge. The constant and plentiful supply of water reduced the need to site watermills on its adjacent tributaries; the main river powered twenty-two mills. The tributaries were only used at locations generally well away from the main river, especially to serve such towns and villages as Haslemere, Chobham and Chertsey.

Other rivers and streams used were the Hogsmill River, which flows northwards from Ewell, the Bourne to the north-west of the county, the Redhill Brook and finally, a small tributary of the River Arun at Forest Green and Ockley. There were of course other mill sites scattered around the county, located on small tributaries.

Other commercially important waterways in Surrey were the Basingstoke Canal and the Wey and Arun Canal which, in conjunction with the Wey Navigation, provided a route from London to the south coast near Chichester. The River Wey Navigation was one of the earliest canals to be constructed in the country when it was made navigable to Guildford in 1633 and to Goldaming in 1763. These canals provided an easy and convenient means of transport for millers and corn merchants alike. Another benefit provided by the Navigation was its constant water level for several watermills situated by it, such as Newark Mill near Ripley and Coxe's Lock Mill at Weybridge.

The waterwheel was the sole power source in a watermill and every piece of machinery was driven directly or indirectly from it. There is no doubt that the inside of a working watermill was a noisy and at times a dangerous environment with spinning shafts, pinions, gearing and seemingly endless movement of revolving leather straps. Outside the mill, and in complete contrast, all that is heard is the creaking of the slowly turning waterwheel and the gentle gushing sound of water entering the wheel pit. To most people the sight of an externally mounted waterwheel adds character to a mill long after it has ceased working.

It is an accepted fact that the Romans first introduced the watermill into Britain and certainly a number of watermills were constructed to feed the conquering troops. The early waterwheels were probably of the undershot variety driving simple machinery on a mechanical basis, unchanged for centuries. Another type of mill was the 'Norse Mill'. These were introduced by visitors from Scandinavia, and consisted of a primitive horizontal waterwheel set at the base of a vertical shaft connected to a pair of millstones above. As these mills had no gearing, the power to turn the millstones was totally dependent upon the amount of water directed onto the vanes of the wheel at its circumference. It was with the introduction of the geared watermill, using a vertical waterwheel, that the craft of the miller became more sophisticated.

Over the years, various eminent engineers, such as Smeaton, applied their knowledge to the craft of milling in an attempt to derive greater mechanical efficiency from different types of waterwheels. Progress advanced rapidly with the advent of cast iron and many wooden waterwheels were replaced in the 19th century.

The various types of waterwheels are classified according to the point of entry of the water onto the wheel, as follows: Undershot, Breastshot (including high and low), Overshot and Pitchback.

The type and construction of watermills throughout the county varies geographically from east to west. As the county lacked a natural supply of durable building stone, the two principal materials were brick and timber. As the River Wey supplied plentiful water, the mills that served the towns of Godalming, Farnham and Guildford tended to be large and extensive and were of substantial construction, notably in brick. Examples exist at Godalming Hatch Mill, Bourne Mill at Farnham, and at the Guildford Town Mill. In the eastern section of the county, the smaller and more 'rural' type predominates: Flanchford Mill, for example, combining brick and weatherboarding.

Although watermills prospered and expanded it was not until the end of the 18th century that brick was used extensively in their construction. The reason for the delay in its introduction was the brick tax, introduced in 1784 and increased again in 1794 and 1803. By the time the tax laws were repealed in 1850 few watermills were being built. It is because of the brick tax that weatherboarded mills became popular, though even then brick-built mills were constructed, with Pixham Mill at Dorking a prime example.

The abundance of brickworks throughout Surrey obviously influenced the choice of materials, but aesthetically, the brick and timber watermill remains the more appropriate (and picturesque) type of mill building suitable for a small county such as Surrey.

The breastshot waterwheel in a poor condition at Flanchford Mill in 1986. (NC)

ABOVE: The overflow shield and waterwheel at Snowdenham Mill in 1939. (RCHME) LEFT: This overshot waterwheel at Heath Mill is rapidly deteriorating. BELOW: The waterwheel at Castle Mill in 1970 prior to restoration of the mill. (MM)

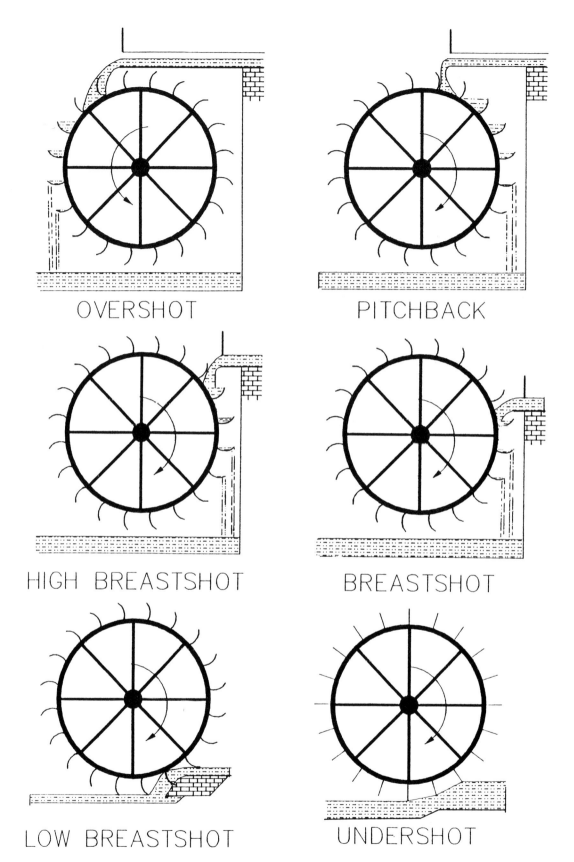

OVERSHOT

PITCHBACK

HIGH BREASTSHOT

BREASTSHOT

LOW BREASTSHOT

UNDERSHOT

Types of waterwheel.

THE MILLER'S CRAFT

The undershot waterwheel is the simplest type, also known as the paddle wheel, and revolves by the direct force of water. This type was first used where there was a small but constant head of water. Around the circumference of the wheel are paddle boards and the wheel is normally externally mounted and just placed in the river or stream direct. The water then passes beneath the waterwheel, striking the bottom blades and setting it in motion. It was more often convenient to position this type of wheel in a mill leat cut from the main river.

The undershot waterwheel was most appropriate in low-lying areas, where there was an all-year-round supply of water and, as the River Wey fulfilled these requirements, many watermills on this river used it. In the Farnham area four of its six mills employed undershot wheels. The power derived from an undershot wheel could be increased by enlarging the diameter or the width, but this could lead to impracticalities in construction and erection. Therefore, few were made of a larger diameter than the surviving undershot waterwheel at Elstead Mill.

The breastshot waterwheel did not appear in this country until the 16th century. In many locations it became more popular than the overshot waterwheel as the latter often required complicated dams and embankments to raise the water to the top of the wheel. Although the breastshot wheel was not entirely without these requirements, its use throughout Surrey was quite extensive.

In a breastshot waterwheel, the water is fed by a pentrough, or pipe, onto the wheel, level with the axle shaft. Variations to this type of wheel were dependent upon the point of access onto the side of the wheel and were generally known as high or low breastshot. The breastshot wheel is either fitted with buckets and driven by the weight of water contained within them or impelled by the water flow onto L-shaped buckets or vanes. This type of wheel was generally used where a substantial water supply could be ponded and controlled and, when working to its maximum power, it could attain approximately 55% mechanical efficiency.

Breastshot waterwheels were mainly large in diameter and in Surrey, the largest extant breastshot wheel is that at Flanchford Mill where the diameter is 19ft 6in with a width of 5ft.

The overshot waterwheel was commonly found in Surrey as an attempt to generate maximum water power from the various tributaries. Its greatest advantage was its mechanical efficiency of 65% and that it only required a small amount of water to turn. Until the end of commercial milling, it was probably used more than any other type.

In the working of an overshot waterwheel, water is fed over the top to fill the buckets. The weight of the water sets the wheel in motion using 'potential energy' as opposed to the 'kinetic energy' employed in turning an undershot wheel. Once the wheel is set in motion, only a small amount of water keeps it turning. To supply the water to the top of the wheel, it was usual to construct an artificial embankment and a millpond.

The pitchback waterwheel works in a similar way to that of a high breastshot wheel, in that the water is fed to a point just below the top of the wheel on its pond side. This results in the wheel moving with the direction of the tail race, which makes it more liable to backwatering. The wheel was also usually set in a sloping water channel to allow the water to flow away quickly; its mechanical efficiency was similar to that of an overshot wheel.

It seems no watermill in Surrey was fitted with such a waterwheel.

There are several typical mills in Surrey. In the south-west of the county both the High Mill at Farnham and Cosford Mill at Thursley contain enough extant machinery to be considered, while at Shalford Mill, near Guildford, the National Trust-owned watermill is complete and open to the public. To the east, Flanchford Mill provides an example of a small rural watermill complete with its machinery, while Coltsford Mill at Hurst Green is the only working Surrey watermill.

However, Haxted Mill, near Edenbridge, provides the best example of a Surrey watermill layout for several reasons. Firstly, as a working watermill museum, it is open to the public and so the mill enthusiast or the casual visitor can see it in operation. Secondly, Haxted Mill contains various types of machinery together with other examples collected from other watermills in the area. Finally, for those interested in the construction of a watermill, the interior provides examples of wood-working techniques dating from the late 17th century.

The first and perhaps most important part of any watermill is the power source, and in the case of Haxted Mill this consists of an external overshot waterwheel 10ft in diameter by 8ft wide. This waterwheel is constructed in iron and is made up of four sets of cruciform arms, and has recently been renovated by the new owners.

Passing through the centre of the waterwheel is the cast iron axle shaft which is fitted into bearings at each end. Attached to this shaft, and revolving in the same plane as the waterwheel, is the iron compass-arm pit wheel, which is known as such because it is accommodated, more often than not, in a pit sunk into the floor of the mill. This facewheel transmits the power derived from the waterwheel to turn the upright shaft by means of a wallower which engages the pit wheel. The purpose of the upright shaft is to provide the motive power source from the pit floor right up to the top of the stone floor, and subsequently to drive the various machinery within the mill. Located on the upright shaft, above the wallower, is the spur wheel which, at Haxted Mill, is of the clasp arm variety constructed in wood, and indeed an excellent and ancient example of its type. The revolving spur wheel drives the 'stone nuts' positioned at its circumference, which in turn are connected by a pinion shaft to the top millstone above. Situated on top of the wooden tun is the hopper, or 'horse', which contains the grain and feeds it into the centre of the revolving millstone. Near the top of the upright shaft is the crown wheel, which is responsible for driving all of the ancillary machinery contained within the mill, such as the sack hoist, flour graders, wheat cleaners, etc.

The operation of a watermill such as Haxted was in the main a simple process of transferring power from the waterwheel through to the top millstone and, providing the machinery was maintained, it offered an economical method of producing flour.

The mechanical process of breaking down wheat kernel to produce flour was basically a simple operation providing that certain controls were followed to ensure the quality of the finished product.

With the advent of mechanical grain threshing machines, the grain could arrive at the mill relatively clean and to a certain extent graded. Nevertheless, all of the grain had to go through a series of processes to ensure that, when it entered the millstones, it was without impurities. The grain would firstly be taken by sack hoist into the storage space, normally in the roof of the mill. The first process passed the grain through a winnower which separated the wheat seed from any remaining chaff, and many of the larger machines utilised an aspirator fan to dispose of the chaff quickly. Although the wheat should arrive at the mill fairly clean, most mills possessed a corn separator and scourer which was the last cleaning process before grinding. On the pit floor at Haxted Mill is such a machine, belt driven from the crown wheel on the stone floor above. This worked by passing the wheat grain through a rotating drum where any remaining chaff or dirt was blown out by a large fan. The grain then passed through ducts containing a large number of magnets which caught pieces of iron or nails, etc. The machine at Haxted Mill was made in the USA by Howes & Ewell and was capable of dealing with 20-30 bushels of corn per hour. Another machine sometimes employed was the smutter, which was used to remove spores of the smut that results from the fungus which attacks British wheat.

After passing through these cleaning processes, the grain was taken up by sack hoist to the top of the mill and placed in a large hopper ready for grinding. Surrey's watermills appear to have a minimum of four grain hoppers, which ensured that the mill could work on a regular and economical basis, while at Godalming Hatch Mill there are no less than seventeen.

From the grain bin the corn was then fed down a cloth spout into a hopper situated on the millstones. The hopper was made of wood and formed part of a framework known as a horse. From the hopper the grain ran down into the shoe, which was hinged at one end of the horse. The front end of the shoe was kept vibrating by a damsel, which was a three-sided iron bar. It was usually driven from below by the runner stone and this bar, hitting against an iron cam on the shoe, made the characteristic 'clacking' noise of a working mill. The rate of flow down the shoe was controlled by a string leading down over a pulley to the miller's position on the ground floor. From below, the miller could then regulate the amount of grain passing into the stones by adjusting the cord on a twist peg located near the meal spout. It was essential to keep the hoppers full when the stones were rotating for, if they ran dry, there was the chance of damage to them or of sparks being generated, which could set off a fire. To warn the miller that a hopper was almost running empty, a bell was attached to a leather strap buried in the grain in the hopper. With an emptying hopper the strap would be released, allowing the bell to drop and hit against the damsel, so warning the miller to refill the hopper or stop the mill.

From the shoe the grain fell into the centre of the runner stone and was then ground on its passage to the circumference of the millstones. It emerged as meal and then fell through a hole on the floor and down a cloth spout, into a sack positioned below. Then the meal was passed through various processes to grade it and, if required, to remove the bran, after which it was ready for delivery to the local baker.

An important factor, to be taken into consideration before the erection of a watermill, was the layout of the watercourses and the position of the waterwheel in relation to the mill building. The simplest method of conveying water to a site was by just using the natural fall of the river or stream and placing the mill and wheel adjacent to it, with a by-pass channel excavated to remove excess water. This method of water engineering can still be seen at Cobham Mill, but even here a complicated weir system had to be constructed to take excess water back to the main river. A second method was to locate the mill across the river itself such as exists, for instance, at High Mill, Farnham. At this location, because the mill is situated in a low-lying position, two by-pass channels were established well before the water entered the mill.

At Coltsford Mill a large and expansive millpond was excavated, and the whole of the waterwheel lies hidden below a high embankment. However, at Coltsford Mill, an ingenious and possibly unique method was employed to remove excess water from the millpond. In the middle of the pond is a large brick-built basin, three metres in diameter, sunk into its base. If the water level increases, with a danger of flooding, the excess is cleared away quickly into the basin and then through a culvert at the side of the mill, without requiring attention from the miller.

Castle Mill at Dorking illustrates the creation of a mill leat cut from the main river. A small overflow weir was constructed across the River Mole, whereby water could be diverted to the mill. The problem with this method was that it offered no protection to the mill when the main river flooded, which it habitually did, and at this location there are several flood level recording marks cut into the side of the mill.

In the western part of the county, the River Wey Navigation was used quite extensively, as in the instance of the Town Mill at Guildford. Here a wide channel was cut from the Navigation, firstly to provide waterpower to the wheel, and secondly, to allow barges to load and unload directly in front of the mill. Lower down the Navigation at Coxe's Lock Mill the water was channelled from the canal to fill a large millpond, although there were litigation threats over the years from the owners of the Navigation for the loss of 'their' water and the reduction of water level when the millpond was being filled up.

Drive machinery at Haxted Mill — LEFT A — Pit Wheel, B — Upright Shaft & C — Wallower, and RIGHT: D — Spur Wheel, E — Stone Nut & F — Drive Pinion. (NC)

CENTRE: Stone floor machinery: G — Pair of Millstones & H — Grain Hopper, and (NC) ABOVE LEFT: ancillary machinery at Haxted Mill: I — Crown Wheel. (NC) RIGHT: A french burr millstone on display at Haxted Mill. (NC) BELOW: A flour grader still *in situ* at Flanchford Mill. (NC)

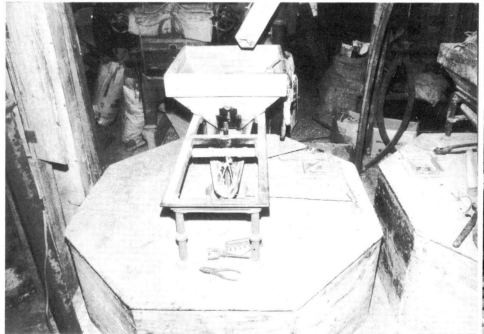

LEFT: Wooden tun and horse on display at Haxted Mill. (NC) RIGHT: The massive wooden upright shaft at Castle Mill in 1970. (MM) BELOW: Hopper, shoe and damsel *in situ* at Coltsford Mill.

ABOVE: Mr Wilfred Heasman, the last working miller in Surrey, dressing a peak millstone at Coltsford Mill. CENTRE: The worn sack hoist spindle at Snowdenham Mill in 1968. BELOW: The water turbine at Godalming Hatch Mill. (NC)

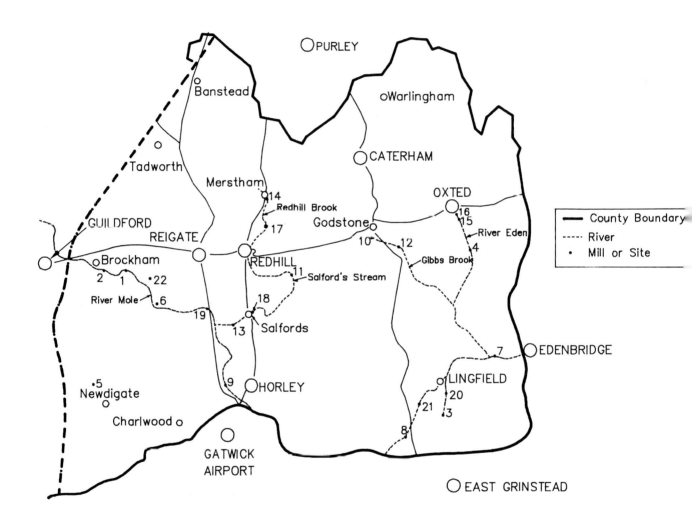

EAST SURREY: 1. Betchworth Mill, 2. Brockham Mill, 3. Clark's Mill, 4. Coltsford Mill, 5. Ewood Mill, 6. Flanchford Mill, 7. Haxted Mill, 8. Hedgecourt Mill, 9. Horley Mill, 10. Ivy Mill, 11. Kings Mill, 12. Leigh Mill, 13. Lodge Mill, 14. Merstham Mill, 15. Oxted Mill, 16. Oxted Upper Mill, 17. Pendell Mill, 18. Salfords Mill, 19. Sidlow Mill, 20. Ware Mill, 21. Wire Mill, 22. Wonham Mill.

THE MILLS OF EAST SURREY

COLTSFORD MILL *Hurst Green*
River Eden TQ 397505 — At the end of a private road leading off Mill Lane.

The external appearance of Coltsford Mill is typical of the type of watermill commonly found in south-east England, namely brick-built to the first floor with weatherboarding above. The mill is situated in a quiet and peaceful corner of Surrey, and is the site of one of the watermills accredited to Oxted during the Domesday Survey. Most important of all, Coltsford Mill is the only working watermill to be found in Surrey.

George Marchant was the miller here until 1866, when the premises were taken over by William Heasman, who had come to this mill from Rowfant Mill, east of Crawley. It is difficult to date the age of the existing buildings but, from an inspection of the materials used, a date near the middle of the 18th century seems likely. The exterior of Coltsford Mill is quite remarkable, with its steep sloping mansard roof set above the high pond embankment. At the front there is a loading door with steps down to ground level, similar to that found at Haxted Mill.

The external iron overshot waterwheel of diameter 16ft 2in by 4ft 1in wide, and the iron pentrough, were both installed in 1866 when Mr Heasman came to the mill. The drive machinery is predominantly iron and also dates from 1866 and is arranged in the standard layout. The iron pit wheel, 10ft in diameter, is cast in two sections with wooden teeth and drove a 3ft diameter wallower. Above the wallower, affixed to the upright shaft, is an iron spur wheel 8ft 4in in diameter with wooden teeth.

Of the existing millstones to be found *in situ* on the stone floor of the mill, three pairs are boxed in wooden tuns, only two of which are capable of use. Of these, one contains peak stones of 4ft diameter, while the other contains french burr stones of the same diameter. Also on the stone floor is one 4ft diameter peak stone still *in situ*, together with three 4ft diameter french burr stones, all of which have been laid out 'face up' for display. All of the stones were supplied by 'Barron & Son' of Gloucester. The two working pairs of stones are fitted with wooden horses and bell alarms. The crown wheel is constructed in iron with wooden teeth and drives various ancillary shafts, the first of which powered a bran duster supplied by a local firm 'B.F. Stapley', and the second a chaff cutter situated in an adjacent barn. On the floor above is a silk flour machine, a semolina roller and a 20ft long flour grader, and throughout the mill there is a system of wooden elevators.

The large millpond has recently been cleared of weed growth and vegetation, with the intention of turning it into a trout fishery. In its centre is a rather unusual overflow basin, which in effect served the same purpose as the more conventional by-pass weir. The great advantage of this basin is that the circumference of 30ft provides an overflow over which excess water can be cleared away quickly.

The last miller here was Wilfred Heasman, a tradesman very much in the traditional mould, who enthused quite naturally about stone ground flour against the modern tasteless white bread. Mr Heasman had to be his own millwright, following the demise of the travelling journeyman so common in the last century. This was fully illustrated some years ago when the waterwheel axle shaft snapped in two for no apparent reason. A hole had to be made in the barn opposite the wheelpit so the broken shaft could be removed and a replacement installed, which weighed 27 cwt.

Coltsford Mill stopped working commercially after the last war, but happily, the mill to this day still grinds a certain amount of flour and animal food, albeit for private use, while the storage space on the ground floor has been converted to a popular restaurant. In May 1988 the mill was advertised for sale and the new owners aim to expand the existing restaurant. They have no plans to modernise or alter the mill itself, thus ensuring that the last working watermill in Surrey remains so.

EWOOD MILL *Newdigate*
Tributary to River Mole TQ 200447 — At the end of Mill Lane

Although the prominence of Ewood as a Wealden Iron site is not forgotten, the history of the corn mill that shared the same site has long been overlooked. Ernest Straker, in his excellent book *Wealden Iron*, describes the early events that took place when an iron furnace was established here in the 16th century.

A survey of the iron workers here in 1574 includes references to a watermill for grinding corn, and the mill survived the closure of the furnace in 1604 as an advertisement in 1771 stated:

'To be sold pursuant to a decree, the freehold estate of Richard Morton late of Reigate, consisting of a farm of about 150 acres, a large pond together with a messuage and corn mill.'

As a corn mill, the site is not mentioned again until the publication of Senex's map of 1729, while later in 1768 Rocque marks it as 'Yew Mill', and finally it is shown on Lindley and Crossley's map as 'Ewood Mill' in 1790. The mill was probably demolished in the early years of the 19th century as the 1st Edition of the Ordnance Survey map along with Greenwood's map of 1823 make no reference to the site. The pond that supplied the iron furnace and the corn mill was one of the largest to be found in the Weald and, because the valley at this point is exceedingly shallow, a large water storage area was required. The pond was drained in 1840 but there are traces of a long bay together with two large culverts through the spillway.

The site is to be found at the end of a bridleway, named Mill Lane, which branches off the junction of Broad Lane with Parkgate Road, and even today the associated earthworks are clearly visible.

FLANCHFORD MILL *Reigate*
Wallace Brook TQ 235479 — South of Flanchford Farm, Flanchford Road.

Flanchford Mill is a small country watermill of a type and construction that was once commonly found in Surrey and south-east England. Unlike its all-brick counterparts, many of which have survived the years, few of the predominantly wooden mills remain intact and therefore it is unusual that Flanchford Mill still survives. Although lying derelict, it contains most of its machinery and the remains of the waterwheel.

The first historical reference to a mill on this site appeared in the 13th century when mention was made of a 'Hartswood Mill' in Buckland Parish while, later in 1527, Sir John Dudley conveyed certain lands included within which was a watermill called 'Flansford Mill'. Thereafter, the estate and the watermill passed to a succession of owners with, for example,

Edward Shelley conveying it in the following year to Sir Thomas Bludder. In 1730, according to a report, an estate known as 'Flanchford' had been in the possession of Cyril Wyche and included with the property were four ponds which provided a plentiful supply of water to drive a mill. From 1730, several owners of the parkland surrounding the Mill are recorded, and it was during that period that the existing mill was built. This is confirmed by an etching in the brickwork in the wall of the pit floor, dated 1768, and it can be assumed that James Scawen, the owner of the estate at the time, was responsible for its construction. Scawen later bequeathed the estate in 1781 to his great-nephew, Sir Peter Burrell, who sold it to William Browne in 1791. Afterwards, the estate passed into the management of William Clutton, whose executors held it well into the 20th century.

The early history of the mill, in terms of ownership, is well recorded but, as to the names of millers, little is known. There is a vague reference to a Peter Caffyn being the miller here in 1850 but little more is known about him, apart from the fact that a miller of the same name was recorded at Horley Mill from 1862 until 1895. What is certain, however, is that in 1863 the miller was Charles Dowlen and it was he who was responsible for installing the new waterwheel in 1870. That was made of wood and breastshot, while the wheel it replaced was smaller in diameter and overshot. Dowlen had moved to Flanchford Mill from Parsonage Mill at Dorking, and upon his death in 1875 his son John took over until 1887, after which Edward Elphick took control. Over the following fifteen years, Elphick became a prosperous corn merchant operating from premises in Reigate. At the turn of the century the mill was just used by the local farmer with a Mr Bartlett the last regular miller to work here. Mr J. Humphery, the farmer at the nearby Santon Farm, was the last person to use the mill, and during the Second World War it finally closed down. At the end, the mill was only used during the winter months as the ailing water supply meant that it was virtually unworkable during the rest of the year.

The diameter of the externally mounted waterwheel is 19ft 6in which, at first glance, would appear rather out of place in such a small mill. Although its width of 5ft is more in keeping with other small mills, the wheel would undoubtedly have been slow-running. Unfortunately, this great waterwheel is rapidly deteriorating and the iron J-buckets have dropped off into the wheelpit shortly, no doubt, to be followed by the rotten framework. For such a small and seemingly insignificant watermill, it contains some unusual machinery layouts. The most interesting feature is that, although the normal arrangement of pit wheel-wallower-spur wheel does exist, it is not driven directly from the waterwheel. On the pit wheel shaft is a cog wheel which takes a parallel drive from the primary pit wheel, which is affixed to the axle shaft of the waterwheel. This most unusual arrangement was necessary when the new waterwheel was installed, to ensure that the millstones revolved the same way as before. The primary pit wheel is cast iron, of diameter 8ft 8in with wooden cogs, while the small iron cog wheel is of 2ft 7in diameter. The secondary pit wheel is also iron and of a diameter of 7ft 3in, and this drove an iron spur wheel of 6ft 9in diameter. The two iron stone nuts are still in position and were lifted in and out of gear by jack rings. The central iron upright shaft is octagonal in shape and drove, on the stone floor, an iron crown wheel of 6ft diameter. This crown wheel has upward facing wooden teeth that engaged a 1ft diameter iron cog on a 3in square shaft which, *via* a linked system of bevel wheels, operated a large flour machine on the stone floor and a small flour grader on the pit floor. Flanchford was a small watermill and only contained two pairs of stones; both pairs are peakstone grit, and well worn. Another interesting and unusual feature is the arrangement of the sack hoist. The hoist was geared directly into the primary pit wheel by a small cog wheel, with the slack in the belt drive taken up by a sliding block moving in an inclined wooden frame. The sack hoist was controlled by pulling the hoist chain up, instead of downwards. In the roof of the mill are six large grain bins set between wooden staging. The mill is constructed in a combination of elm, oak and brick to the first floor with tarred weatherboarding above.

Attached to the mill are two brick built cottages, which were added to in the 1930s when the mill was virtually closed down. The once attractive millpond had to be drained following flood damage to the sluice gates in 1968, and for many years the pond became a mass of vegetation. In 1987 the owner set about clearing the millpond, restoring it to its former idyllic glory, and now it is used to breed trout.

HAXTED MILL *Haxted*
River Eden TQ 419455 — Adjacent to the Lingfield to Edenbridge Road

Of all the remaining mill buildings in Surrey, Haxted must be one of the most interesting, especially since it is now a watermill museum. Inside you can observe the structural make-up of a working watermill, parts of which date back to the late 17th century. The mill is constructed in two separate phases, the western half built in 1680 on 14th century foundations, while the eastern section was built in 1794.

Haxted Mill was always a corn mill and is built of brick to the first floor with weatherboarding above, all under a matched pair of mansard roofs with a projecting lucomb on the western half. The mill is adjacent to the Lingfield–Edenbridge Road three quarters of a mile from the county boundary with Kent. The water from the River Eden is ponded to the rear of the mill by means of an artificial embankment but, unusually, the mill does not form part of it, as the dam served only as a method for the storage of water.

The waterwheel is externally mounted, affixed to the western side of the mill and constructed in cast iron, overshot, with a diameter of 10ft with a width of 8ft, and with four sets of arms. Recently, new owners have extensively refurbished the mill and millrace as well as fitting new steel buckets to the waterwheel. Inside the mill, sturdy oak timbers, hand adzed in the western half, complement the predominantly wooden machinery. Most of this is of considerable age and of special interest is the 6ft diameter clasp arm spur wheel along with the upright shaft below the spur wheel, cracked badly during the 1914–18 war and rather crudely repaired using hooped iron. During the conversion to a working mill museum, the damaged section was replaced by an iron fabricated component. The drive from the waterwheel turns an iron pit wheel of 7ft 10in diameter, which meshes with an iron wallower attached to the upright shaft. On the floor above is a wooden clasp arm crown wheel of 4ft 9in diameter. The mill contains three pairs of french burr stones arranged in a normal layout, but there is also *in situ* another pair located away from the upright shaft. This pair of stones was overdriven from a shaft off the crown wheel but, when put into operation, the extra power required brought the whole mill to a standstill! This pair of stones was promptly abandoned.

Contrary to local tradition, this is not a Domesday mill site as Haxted, at the time, was under oak forest. From the 13th century, Haxted was an estate of some size and importance and the first reference to a mill here is in 1361 when it was left by Reginal de Cobham to his wife, Joan. He died of the plague in 1362 and his wife, on her death, left the mill to her son, Reginald. The Stanford family were major occupiers of the mill during the 18th and 19th centuries and they used this mill in conjunction with the Town Mill in the centre of Edenbridge. William Laker was the miller until 1838, but from then on the Stanfords ran the mill themselves with James, then Joseph, continuing until 1882, after which another James became the miller. He was followed by Thomas Stanford, who worked the mill until his death in 1944, after which it was sold. Although the Second World War provided an uplift in trade, the vibrations from the upright shaft threatened to shake the mill to pieces. After the war the mill continued working for a few years, but commercial milling was never seriously considered here again.

The mill and the surrounding land were purchased by Mr Woodrow in 1949 mainly for the purpose of setting up kennels but, after some deliberation, he embarked on an ambitious project to create a watermill museum. After a considerable amount of time and effort the museum was opened in April 1966.

Haxted Mill is fortunately preserved and once again a well-known landmark, and is open to the public on most days during the summer months.

HEDGECOURT MILL *Felbridge*
Eden Brook TQ 358404 — At the end of Mill Lane north of Copthorne Road.

Hedgecourt Mill was on the artificial embankment of one of the largest millponds to be found in south-east England, with a surface area of 42 acres. Contrary to popular belief, there is no evidence to suggest that this millpond ever had associations with the Wealden iron industry widespread in this part of the country. In contrast to the size of the millpond, the last mill to work on this site was small, but more important, Hedgecourt Pond acted as a 'pen pond' for the storage of water for the much larger Wire Mill.

Hedgecourt Mill was referred to as a corn mill as early as the days of Queen Elizabeth I and was also marked on John Seller's map of 1679. The last mill to occupy this site was constructed towards the end of the 17th century, and contained only two pairs of stones. The waterwheel, 12ft 6in in diameter by 6ft wide, was fed with water *via* a pipe connected to the pond, on the other side of the track that passed the front door of the mill.

The mill is marked on all contemporary maps from the 17th century but, apart from these, little documentation appears to exist. John Stone was the miller here in 1822, and he was followed by L. Hardy, who was also using the Horne windmill. From at least the 1900s, and no doubt some time before that, the mill was worked in conjunction with the nearby Wire Mill, just over a mile downstream.

By the middle of the 1930s Hedgecourt Mill was disused and, being of fairly ancient construction and in an exposed location, the mill building quickly fell into ruin. A pen and ink sketch, drawn in the 1920s, showed it was of stone construction to the first floor, with weatherboarding up to the hipped tiled roof and overall typically rural in appearance. It is still possible to see the framework of the iron overshot waterwheel affixed to a now rotting wooden axle shaft, and a 9ft 6in diameter pit wheel.

The mill is reached by a narrow road, named Mill Lane, that branches off northwards from the Felbridge — Copthorne road. Just before the site is the miller's cottage, although it has now been extensively enlarged into a house of some size.

HORLEY MILL *Horley*
River Mole TQ 271434 — Adjacent to Mill Lane

There are many early references to the watermill at Horley, the first of which appears in a deed of the 13th century. In this Robert, son of Walter de Horleia, granted the mill to his son Alfred at a rent of a silver mark, and a meadow by the mill at a rent of 16d. A considerable dispute arose here in 1429 between the Abbot of Chertsey and Reginald de Cobham over the maintenance of the river bank from Rowley Mill to Horley Mill. Reginald de Cobham was so incensed at being instructed to carry out the work that he disclaimed his responsibility in the Parish Church at Horley before all the parishioners!

With the dissolution of the monasteries in 1538 all property belonging to them was confiscated by the Crown and the ownership of Horley Mill, with the manor of Horley, changed hands. The manor was then initially held by Sir Nicholas Carew until he lost favour with

Henry VIII and was beheaded, the land then passing to Sir Robert Southwell until he sold it to Robert Bristow in 1544. The mill did not remain long in the ownership of the Bristow family, for it was sold again, this time to John Kerrell and his son Nicholas in 1586.

For the next one hundred years little mention is made of it apart from the fact that John Gardner, the miller, was brought before the Surrey Quarter Sessions in 1661 for taking an 'excessive toll of flour'. In 1710, Thomas Dabner purchased Horley Mill from John Heaver of Reigate for 'one guinea, plus a further £248 18s 6d', and the property was described as a 'messuage, watermill, stables, orchard and four acres of meadow land'. In 1760 James Constable married Mary Dabner, sister of Thomas, and bought up all the family shares in the mill and, when he died in 1778, his son, also named James, took over as miller. He is listed as a creditor of a bankrupt farmer in 1814. Upon his death in 1838, his sons Charles and William took over, and one of the first things they did was to install a steam engine to assist the waterwheel. It is also probable that they were responsible for erecting the last, and by far the biggest, mill on the site. Upon the retirement of Charles Constable in 1862 the mill was put up for sale, according to an advertisement. It stated that the breastshot waterwheel was 18ft in diameter, and that the mill was capable of grinding 25-30 loads per week, with storage facilities for 1100 sacks of flour.

The mill was purchased by Christ's Hospital, and Peter Caffyn (also at Three Bridges) was the miller; later in 1895 the mill was again up for sale, according to this sale notice:

'Horley Mill, Surrey. To be let on a lease or sold, this desirable Steam and Water Flour Mill, with corn stores, miller's house, two cottages, stabling etc. The mill is fitted with wheat and oat stones, all requisite wheat cleaning tackle, and Simon's reduction rolls and centrifugals, the whole working automatically. Apply to the foreman on the premises, to the Clerk, Christ's Hospital, E.C.'

In 1899 the mill was once more up for sale, but a new tenant could not be found and it closed down and was demolished in 1926. Following the regrading of the river and the construction of a new road bridge in 1959, there are few remains to be seen apart from the brick retaining wall of the wheel pit.

The site is in Mill Lane, just upstream from the road bridge, adjacent to a house called 'Horley Mill', while about fifty yards from the mill site stands the old mill house. This is a picturesque red-brick building surmounted by a bell turret, which once held a bell used to summon the whole district whenever a serious fire occurred.

IVY MILL *Godstone*
Gibbs Brook TQ 348513 — Adjacent to Ivy Mill Lane

This mill was identified in the Domesday Survey as the mill at 'Chevington', and that still lingers on in the name of a farm not far from the site of the mill.

John Aubrey, who wrote so much about Surrey in the 17th century, mentions the manor of Stangrave 'to which a mill belonged', and in 1674 Stangrave passed into the ownership of Thomas Northey, whose son built Ivy House in Bletchingley, and from which the mill earned its name. A report on its condition in 1680 stated that rebuilding was essential owing to the poor state of the timberwork, and this advice was taken by Thomas Northey in that same year. A lease, dated 1706, gives John Hills of Godstone as the miller when the rental was assessed at £22 per annum. Following the death of Thomas Northey in 1705, the estate passed into the ownership of his son, also named Thomas, but he had no male heirs and eventually his three daughters sold the whole Stangrave estate to Sir Kenrick Clayton. A descendant of Sir Kenrick, one William, in turn sold the estate to Philip de Clermont in 1890, except for the mill, which he retained until Sir William Greenwell bought it in 1907.

The first miller in the 19th century was Richard Dewdney, who was granted a 'messuage, watermill, lands and a windmill' in a document dated 1817, for a period of fourteen years at a rental of £100. Dewdney retained his interest in the two mills until 1841, but by 1847 the wind and watermill had both been leased to Henry Rose. Rose remained in control of both until Russell Hall took over the tenancy. Bromley Hall had taken over by 1903 and ran it until about 1915, but later in 1924 the mill was destroyed by fire, two years after it stopped working.

The last mill to occupy this site was brick-built and consisted of an assortment of buildings of varying height with a half-hipped roof. The pond embankment at this point was of a height that suggested an overshot waterwheel, but disaster struck the mill in 1909 when heavy storms caused the bank of the millpond to burst, and drain the pond complement. The embankment was repaired and the mill continued working until 1922.

Nothing but the stone footings remain, while on the opposite side of the road is the mill house, dating from 1698.

KING'S MILL *South Nutfield*
Tributary to River Mole TQ 299489 — Adjacent to King's Mill Lane.

The precise location of the watermill, referred to as 'Notfell' in the Domesday Survey, is unknown, but its value of 2s indicates that it was a small one compared to other valuations. An article in the journal of the Bourne Society speculates on another mill site at South Nutfield. The existing King's Mill was erected in the middle half of the 18th century, and there is no reason to believe that there was a mill on this site before then. John Senex does not mark a mill here on his map of 1729 and five years earlier no mill is shown on the large scale Budgen's estate map of the area.

There appears to be strong evidence to support the theory of an earlier watermill site at South Nutfield. On the 1st Edition of the Ordnance Survey 1/2500 map, published in 1869, an area of land to the south of Hale Farm would appear to form a most suitable site for a mill. The river at this point has been straightened to form what looks like a mill leat and even in 1869, long after the mill had disappeared, sluice gates were evident. Now, the grassed area of Redhill Aerodrome has obliterated this possible site, referred to in 1359 as 'Hale Mill'.

The present site of King's Mill is possibly no more than 200-250 years old and the first reference to this mill is to be found on John Rocque's map of 1768.

The first known owner of King's Mill is Thomas Burt, who purchased it for £200 in January 1810. Six years later, James Dives took over the tenancy on a one year lease, which was renewed in 1818 for a further 21 years at a rental of £12 per annum. Thomas Beale was the next occupier from 1831 until 1851, whereafter George Dives, a relation of James Dives, took over. During his occupation Dives carried out extensive alterations and modifications to the machinery. Edmund Nye was the next occupier, having also been the miller at the nearby Salfords Mill since 1855. Later, the mill was up for sale and a valuation gives an insight into the contents.

'The property consists of a timber built and slated watermill situate about three quarters of a mile from Nutfield Station on the South Eastern Railway, consisting of three floors and fitted with three pairs of stones, wheat cleaner, oat crusher with a small office on the first floor. The mill is driven by water power and is fitted with all the necessary water gearing and iron waterwheel. There is also a Cornish boiler with engine attached, but these are not at present in working order. We understand there is sufficient water power to run the mill practically the whole year. Adjoining is a chaff house with loft over. In the rear is an enclosure of pasture land about 6 acres in extent and together with the millpond, makes the whole area upwards of seven acres. We understand there is a small tithe on the property.'

A valuation of £1900 was made on the mill, which also included two small cottages nearby; despite the claim that there was sufficient water available all year round, this is dubious.

The site was purchased by W.H. Vincent, in whose family it remained until the mill ceased working using water power in 1944. The mill still continued as a corn mill until 1963, although only animal feed was produced, using machinery powered by electricity. A shop in Station Road, Redhill, 'Bacons Corn Stores', was run in conjunction with the mill.

The externally mounted iron overshot waterwheel was constructed to an unusual design in that the width of the wheel (11 feet) was greater than the diameter (9 feet) and, as Hillier aptly stated when he observed this wheel *in situ*, it was to a design more suggestive of a steam roller. The wheel was fed by a wooden pentrough, and powered three-pairs of stones.

The mill was built to a style and construction commonly found in south-east England and Surrey, and typically, it was not a large mill, but its weatherboarding and magnificent mansard roof certainly give it an air of distinction. Two bedstones are all that remain of the machinery, but no one entering the mill can fail to be impressed by the massive oak timbers to be seen in the pit floor area.

King's Mill lies adjacent to King's Mill Lane on the perimeter of Redhill Aerodrome. Although the millpond has dried up and the river has been diverted away from the mill, the building still stands proudly on a site first established here in the middle of the 18th century.

LEIGH MILL *Godstone*
Gibbs Brook TQ 361509 — At the end of a small turning south-east of Godstone Road.

Leigh Mill has been converted to an attractive private residence secluded within twenty-two acres of assorted woodlands, paddocks and lakes. The mill site was known in its early days as 'Godstone Mill' and produced gunpowder as well as flour. This is an ancient site, but surprisingly, the Domesday Survey shows no mill in Langham manor, within which it was situated.

An inventory of the manor of Marden in 1349, the year of the Black Death, clearly illustrates the effect that the plague had on rural communities such as Godstone. An inventory item reads 'A watermill, rickety and ruinous, worth nothing this year because all the customers who used the mill are dead, so there is no custom and it stands empty and no one will rent it'. Obviously, the mill had been rebuilt when Stephen and Christene att Lee became the tenants in 1423. The Lee family prospered and by 1496 Richard att Lee occupied a large house near the mill, later known as Lee Place, the predecessor of Leigh Place, which is near the mill site.

By the beginning of the 17th century gunpowder was being manufactured here under the direction of George Evelyn, with his son as the occupier in 1613. On 1 November 1635 the appointment of powder-maker to King Charles I was given to Samuel Cordwell and George Collins, tenants of the Chilworth Gunpowder Mills near Guildford. The site then reverted to corn milling, as indicated on John Senex's map of 1729. From 1841 the mill was in the control of Benjamin Kelsey who, by 1850, had a similar interest at Gomshall Mill. The Kelsey family continued milling at Leigh Mill until 1922, after which Jesse Dadswell took over until it ceased working in 1934.

Fortunately, when the mill was converted to a private residence, the waterwheel was retained along with some of the pit machinery. The waterwheel is overshot, constructed of iron with a diameter of 16ft 8in by 4ft wide. The wooden launder that conveyed the water to the wheel is still extant but, along with the waterwheel, it is slowly deteriorating. It is recorded that Leigh Mill contained only three-pairs of stones which, considering its size, seems rather surprising.

MERSTHAM MILL *Merstham*

Tributary to Redhill Brook TQ 291535 — Obliterated by the M25 Motorway. Site was east of the High Street.

This is obviously the site of a Domesday Mill for it was recorded then that the mill at 'Merstan' was worth 30d. In 1399, Merstham formed part of the Reigate Hundred and was in the ownership of the Archbishop of Canterbury, but it is not until William Jolliffe purchased most of the manor of Merstham in 1784, that mention is made of the watermill. Part of the sale transactions included a 'watermill, dwelling house and twelve and a half acres of land let to Thomas Durrant at an annual rental of £28.'

An interesting court case held in 1810 highlighted one of the most common problems associated with the supply of water to a mill. The owners of the nearby stone quarry had constructed a tunnel to drain excess water, but this had resulted in the stream that fed the mill completely drying up. Durrant, the lessee of the mill, brought action against the owners of the quarry, Messrs Banks and Jollife, and the subsequent court case resulted in a verdict for the plaintiff, who was awarded £2,200 in compensation.

In the early 1840s James Dive was the occupier, having moved from King's Mill at South Nutfield, but quite soon after that the tenancy went to Michael Stacey. The mill remained in the Stacey family until 1898, after which George Lockyer became the miller. He was followed in 1900 by Samuel Baker who was here until closure in 1903. By then the mill was in need of major repairs, which were not carried out, and subsequently the building became derelict before it was demolished in 1938. The mill was situated in meadow land to the north of the village, with the water coming from a spring near St Katherine's Church, which lies opposite the site.

Nothing remains of the millpond or the footings of the mill, as the M25 Motorway now crosses the site and has drastically altered the appearance of the immediately surrounding area. The only remaining feature associated with the site is Old Mill Lane, which originally ran from the former line of the main highway, Quality Street, down to the mill, but even this small lane was reduced in length following the construction of the Croydon–Reigate turnpike in 1808.

OXTED MILL *Oxted*

River Eden TQ 397505 — In Spring Lane south-west of the High Street.

Oxted Mill was, in its latter working years, two self-contained flour mills attached to each other located on an ancient mill site. Both mills were fed off the same branch of the stream that issues from the escarpment of the North Downs just to the north of Oxted. When the mills were working, the stream was ponded, but it has since dried up and is now overgrown.

The older mill here is of three storeys in red brick under a slate roof with a projecting lucomb over the ground floor entrance, while the adjacent roller mill is similar in construction but larger in size. The older mill was built sometime in the mid-19th century, while the roller mill commenced working on 12 June 1893 at 3pm.

James Brooker was the miller by 1826 and he is described in the local trade directory as a 'banker, coal and hay merchant'. The mill passed from Samuel Jenner to Thomas Brand in 1882, and by 1888, William Heasman was using it and was responsible for constructing the roller mill, which he ran in conjunction with nearby Coltsford Mill.

The older of the two mills was powered by an iron overshot waterwheel that became enclosed when the roller mill was constructed. This wheel is still *in situ* although most of its buckets have rusted away. The wheel is 12ft in diameter by 5ft 6in wide, mounted on a square axle shaft. In the pit floor all the primary drive machinery remains in good condition, and appears to date from the end of the 19th century. The 9ft diameter pit wheel has wooden teeth while the wallower is iron. Above the wallower is the 8ft diameter iron spur wheel which again has wooden teeth. The iron upright shaft is octagonal at its base, square through the wallower and spur wheel, with the bearing set in the joists of the stone floor above.

The roller mill, built in 1893, has all the external architectural features of a typically late Victorian building and, apart from the extant turbine, is now completely devoid of machinery. This building housed a three or four sack roller mill plant, manufactured and installed by Henry Simon of Manchester. The system was powered by a Girard Turbine made by W. Gunther & Sons of Oldham. The turbine has a diameter of 48in and produced just over 34hp at 60 rev/min. At the back of the mill, a door leads into the turbine room, where the drive pinion and crown wheel are located.

When flour milling ceased altogether in August 1951, both buildings were purchased by a car accessory firm. The buildings are in a delightful location and, resting against the front of the mill, there are five french burr millstones, all 4ft in diameter, supplied by Hughes & Sons of London. Just to the west of the mill, and in complete contrast, stands the mill cottage, which dates back to the early 18th century.

OXTED UPPER MILL *Oxted*
River Eden TQ 387522 — Located south of the High Street, Old Oxted.

Two watermills are mentioned in the Domesday Survey for Oxted and three later, in the inquisition of Roland of Oxted in 1291.

Upper Mill is shown on Senex's map of 1729 but by 1768, the date of Rocque's map of Surrey, the mill apparently no longer existed. No early references appear to exist and the site has faded into complete obscurity. The mill was to the rear of where the Wheatsheaf public house now stands at the east end of the High Street in Old Oxted. In 1817 a John Cole is recorded as building some cottages on the land that once was 'the millpond'.

SALFORDS MILL *Salfords*
Salfords Stream TQ 281467 — Adjacent to Horley Road.

It was not until the 19th century that the mill was established but exactly when is unclear. On a map showing the route of the proposed railway through the Redhill area the mill is marked as such. In the Horley poor rate account of 1800 a mill is accredited to Stephen Allen, but it is crossed out, indicating that it was not yet in use. From at least 1768 Salvers Farm occupied the site, yet by 1805 the mill was definitely in use, while much later in 1855 it was occupied by Edward Nye, who continued as miller until at least 1882. By 1887 J.A. Burrows was the occupier but in February of that year the mill was destroyed by fire, according to an entry in a trade magazine. Using the insurance money from the fire, the mill was rebuilt and this time a massive five floor building housing a Tattersall Roller system was installed, powered by the large external waterwheel. A 10hp high and low pressure beam engine was later supplied and installed by Thomas Horn & Son, a well-known firm of engineers and millwrights based in Waterloo Road in London, with the boiler supplied by Whitmore & Binyon.

In June 1896 J. Burrows & Son were declared bankrupt, which is surprising considering the modern and up-to-date mill under their control, and in the following year the lease was advertised in a trade magazine, part of which referred to a 'Mill to let which is fitted with steam engine and boiler, waterwheel (out of order), four pairs of stones and a strong hurst framing. Tattersall three break rollers, wheat cleaners etc.'

The lease was taken up by the Seventh Day Adventist organisation who, towards the end of the 19th century, proposed to supply its members in England with health foods then only obtainable in the USA but, owing to financial restrictions, failed in their endeavours.

36

Nevertheless, certain leaders of the organisation later formed the London Health Food Company, under the guidance of one Dr Kellogg, who was the Medical Superintendent of the local sanatorium in Battle Creek, Michigan. The Seventh Day Adventist Organisation commenced operations at Salfords Mill under the name of the International Health Organisation Ltd. Soon the business was in full production at the mill, using a machine for flaking wheat, imported from the USA and, apart from wheat-flaked cereals, the firm also produced health biscuits and nut food. However, on 16 August 1900 the mill was completely destroyed by fire. Following the release of the fire insurance money, the business was transferred to Birmingham, but this could not take away the fact that Salfords Mill was the first mill in the country to specifically produce breakfast cereals.

The mill consisted of five floors of brick under a tiled roof, with access to the adjacent London to Brighton Road.

The fire destroyed all the machinery and utensils and the remaining brickwork gradually crumbled away until the site was eventually cleared. Today a large hotel occupies it and even the sluice gates have gone.

SIDLOW MILL *Sidlow*
River Mole TQ 258470 — Adjacent to Doversgreen Road.

This is an ancient mill site that, if records are to be believed, reputedly dates from Saxon times. The mill is said to take its name from a Saxon woman called Sidilufa, though when she lived is not documented.

By 1279 the mill was known as *Sidala-wemelle* and later in 1332 it was called *Sydelove* when a man named Roberto paid 2s 8½d in tax. A lease drawn up during the reign of Richard I refers to a grant from Hamlyn de Warren to Robert de Compa of land and a mill called *Sideluna*, all at an annual rental of 22s.

In 1412 the miller at Sidlow, John Greyning, was fined '2d as a common butcher for taking an excessive toll of grain' at Banstead Manorial Court, while later, in 1432, the miller was paying tithes to Richard Arundell, the Lord of the Manor. Again in 1533 mention is made of the mill following a report on the decaying timber bridge next to it. The names of millers resident at a wind or watermill are commonplace following the introduction of trade directories in the middle of the 19th century, but in the preceding centuries such records are sparse indeed. It is therefore unusual that the Sidlow millers are well recorded between 1576 and 1680: 1576–Richard Gander, 1587–Richard Cuddington, 1623–John Cuddington, 1680–George Cuddington, and in a lease dated 1682 the mill lay vacant following the death of the widow of John Cuddington. Also included in the lease was an orchard on the north side of the mill. Little more is known about it apart from the fact that John Heaver was a later miller here.

Sidlow Mill is marked on John Rocque's map of 1768 as 'Sidlunt Mill', but on Lindley & Crosley's reliable map of 1790 it is not shown at all.

The reason for the closure of this mill in the latter years of the 18th century are unclear. In general this was the beginning of a time of expansion for the agricultural community of Surrey and many watermills were constructed or extended. The site at Sidlow, no doubt prone to flooding, was immediately next to the London–Brighton road which was turnpiked in 1775, thereby providing reasonable communication.

The remains of the mill leat are still just visible on the north side of the river, at a point where the busy A217 crosses the River Mole.

WARE MILL *Lingfield*

Tributary to River Medway TQ 395423 — By a private road, south of Racecourse Road.

Ware Mill was certainly a corn mill in the 19th century, and no other references exist to show that the site served any other purpose. Some confusion over the correct name for the mill exists, as it formed part of the Weir estate and accordingly it is referred to in some circumstances are 'Weir Mill'. The Ordnance Survey maps and trade directories, however, always refer to it as 'Ware Mill'.

Millers here during the 19th century were 1838–William Laker, 1866–James Laker, 1878–William Stanford, and finally in 1882, Albert Stanford. In 1885 the surrounding land, including the mill, was up for sale, and the sale notice referred to a large millpond and overshot waterwheel, driving two pairs of stones.

The estate was sold and part of it converted to a racecourse (Lingfield Park), which necessitated demolishing the mill and draining the large millpond. The small stream still meanders through the site and, at one point, just past the old mill house, there remain some stone footings, possibly the last traces of the mill.

WIRE MILL *Newchapel*

Eden Brook TQ 368418 — Adjacent to a private road leading off the Eastbourne Road.

To the south-west of Lingfield, in an angle formed by the main road from East Grinstead to Newchapel, there stands Wire Mill. In the Middle Ages it was a forge, which worked in conjunction with Warren Furnace, to the north of Crawley Down. John Thorpe was in charge of both sites then, when they were in the ownership of John Gage.

In the East Grinstead Carriers' Accounts there are references in April and May 1769 to bringing coals from Brail, Lewes, to Woodcock Forge, but by 1788 it is described as a wire mill. The site continued as such into the early 19th century, according to a newspaper article: 'To be Let, a large head of water flowing over 26 acres, together with a mill which has lately been occupied as a wire mill'.

The site is marked on all of the popular maps from 1729 until 1823 as 'Woodcock Hammer', after which it became 'Woodcock Mill', thus designating the newly constructed corn mill. James Jenner is recorded as the first miller with John Sanders taking over in 1838. He was followed by Thomas Brand, who continued until 1882, and it appears that David Dadswell was in control when the mill closed down in 1912. The mill was then advertised for sale according to an article that appeared in a trade magazine: 'A valuable freehold property, an old established corn and flour mill, three miles from East Grinstead, brick and timber built under a slate roof. Two overshot waterwheels and a picturesque residence. A lake and some old cottages. All at £2000'.

The building was used at first by a fishing club but later in 1934 it was converted to a hotel and then a country club in 1962. The mill building, now devoid of any machinery, is of three floors, brick and weatherboarded, under a slate roof with a lucomb projecting out over the private road that passes the front of the mill.

WONHAM MILL *Reigate*

Shag Brook TQ 224496 — Adjacent to Trumpetshill Road.

A photograph of Wonham Mill, dated 1895, shows it was a substantial structure; within twenty-five years, two major building alterations had taken place.

The site at Wonham is to be found beside a narrow winding lane that connects Reigate Heath with Betchworth. A small tributary, called the Shag Brook, provided the necessary water to fill three millponds to the north of the mill. The tail race from the mill passes under the road and connects with the River Mole, some 100 yards away.

The existing mill building is probably on the site of a Domesday Mill for, in 1199, the mill belonged to the manor of Wonham. By 1328 it belonged to Reigate Priory and remained so until the Dissolution in 1536.

In 1845, Michael Bowyer was the tenant and records show that the business remained within the family until 1930. William took over from his father in 1862, he in turn leaving it to Ernest Bowyer in about 1890. It was Ernest Bowyer who was responsible for changing the type and form of the milling operation. It is recorded in a trade magazine that a Simon Roller mill had been installed powered by a 16hp Hornsby oil engine, although the overshot waterwheel was retained. In January 1896, a fire broke out in the engine room and only prompt attention restricted the damage to £30. At the same time, the Bowyer family were working the nearby windmills at Trumpets Hill and Reigate Heath.

The large milling concern of H.A. Trower took over the mill in 1908 and, six years later, it was again enlarged. A four storey brick extension was added to the main mill building and the former stable block was demolished and replaced by a small brick building. In 1930 milling ceased and the goodwill of the business was acquired by the Millers' Mutual Association. In 1937 the surviving machinery was purchased by a German scrap metal merchant and, during the Second World War, the buildings were requisitioned by the Ministry of Food and used for grain storage.

Since the war, Wonham Mill has been used for the storage of animal feedstuffs, although a little oat crushing is occasionally carried out. The only attractive part of an undistinguished group of buildings is the mill house, which dates from the early 18th century.

OTHER EAST SURREY WATERMILL SITES

Betchworth Mill (TQ 212496)
Mention is made of a fulling mill here in 1299 but in 1634, reference is made to a parcel of land besides the River Mole, that once held a watermill.

Brockham Mill (TQ 199498)
A small building next to the River Mole is marked on the 1634 map of the manor of Betchworth. There are visible remains of the tail race.

Clark's Mill (TQ 392403)
The site is marked on Rocque's map of 1768 but little other information exists.

Lodge Mill (TQ 275463)
A site was established here in the 13th century marked 'Toddes Mill' on the Christ's Hospital land.map of 1602. It is not mentioned 30 years later in a property list. Remains of the mill race are still visible, next to Salford's Stream.

Pendell Mill (TQ 311518)
An early mill site, next to the Redhill Brook, this was a fulling mill. All references cease at the end of the 17th century; the site is next to the M25 Motorway.

Two other unnamed water-powered mills in East Surrey were the bone mill at Godstone, on the Gibbs Brook (TQ 364505) — the buildings were demolished in 1971 — and a fulling mill east of Sidlow on the Salfords Stream (TQ 267466). This mill provided employment for the poor in the Parishes of Reigate, Horley and Nutfield. The brick footings are still visible.

40

FAR LEFT: The attractive group of buildings at Leigh Mill; LEFT: following closure in 1934, the waterwheel is slowly rusting away. BELOW LEFT: Coltsford Mill, the last working watermill in Surrey, (RP) and ABOVE: a view across the millpond in 1978. BELOW: The overflow basin provided a quick method of clearing away excess water.

ABOVE: Mill equipment advertisement.

41

ABOVE: Haxted Mill in the early 1900s, (RP) and BELOW: restored as
a working watermill museum. The waterwheel to the right of the mill
came from a Cornish tin mine. (NC)

ABOVE: The Wire Mill up for sale in 1912. BELOW: Oxted Mill in the early 1990s with both mills at work. (RP)

LEFT: Oxted Mill converted into offices; RIGHT: The iron overshot waterwheel has almost rusted away.
BELOW: Ivy Mill at the turn of the century. (RP)

ABOVE: King's Mill in 1966 before its conversion into offices. (SPD)
LEFT: It was at Salfords Mill that the first breakfast cereals were
produced. RIGHT: Horley Mill, a large and once powerful mill, lying
derelict in 1904. (JS)

ABOVE: Wonham Mill in 1895, with various building extensions clearly visible; BELOW: one of the millponds there.

ABOVE: Flanchford Mill in 1870 with the newly installed waterwheel. The old wheel lies on its side by the wheelpit. LEFT: The view across the millpond to Flanchford Mill in 1910. (JS) RIGHT: Flanchford Mill lying derelict in 1986. The large waterwheel has since collapsed and the structural condition of the mill is in some doubt. (NC)

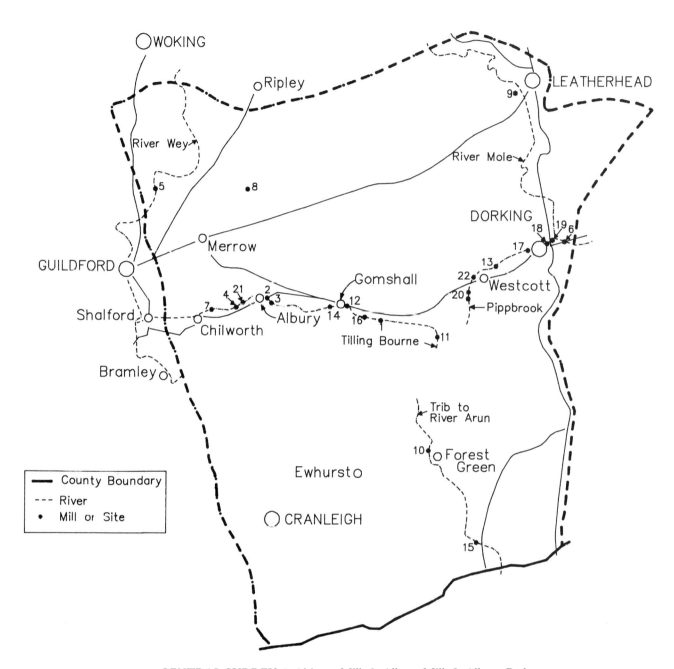

CENTRAL SURREY: 1. Abinger Mill, 2. Albury Mill, 3. Albury Park Mill, 4. Bottings Mill, 5. Bowers Mill, 6. Castle Mill, 7. Chilworth Mill, 8. Clandon Mill, 9. Fetcham Mill, 10. Forest Green Mill, 11. Friday St. Mill, 12. Gomshall Mill, 13. Milton Court Mill, 14. Netley Mill, 15. Oakwood Mill, 16. Paddington Mill, 17. Parsonage Mill, 18. Pippbrook Mill, 19. Pixham Mill, 20. Rookery Mills, 21. Upp. Postford Mill, 22. Westcott Mill.

THE MILLS OF CENTRAL SURREY

ABINGER MILL *Abinger*
Tilling Bourne TQ 110470 — Adjacent to Abinger Lane south of the A25.

This mill site dates back to the end of the 11th century and, similarly to other mills on the Tilling Bourne, it was utilised for various industrial purposes. Gunpowder production took place until at least 1622 when the mills were in the tenancy of George Bromell. Later on in the same year the mill was converted to producing small copper household utensils, with Henry Deane as the first tenant. However, by 1667 the copper trade had diminished and the site then reverted to the more common purpose of producing flour.

At various times Abinger Mill worked in conjunction with Paddington Mill, a short distance downstream for, in an agreement dated 1750 between the owner, Eprian Dabner, and the tenant, John Furlonger, both mills were let together at a yearly rent of £24. In 1845 Thomas Evershed was the tenant of Abinger Mill and he remained in occupation until 1874. In 1851 the Water Resources Survey recorded it as containing two pairs of stones and working on average nine hours per day, producing 40 sacks of flour per week. Arthur Crane took over the tenancy in 1874 and continued until its closure in the early 1890s when the Ordnance Survey 1/2500 map of 1895 marks it as disused.

The mill was of ancient construction with three floors of brick under a tiled roof and the outward appearance of a typical small rural watermill with the top of the roof just above the level of the large millpond.

Abinger Mill was demolished in the early years of this century and, although some walling remains, the once extensive millpond has disappeared under a forest of vegetation. The attractive 17th century millhouse has survived, its gardens open to the public twice a year.

ALBURY MILL *Albury*
Tilling Bourne TQ 053479 — In The Street.

Albury Mill stands on a site which is recorded as far back as 1255, when John Weston conveyed to Thomas Weston a house, watermill and half an acre of land. The Weston family lived in the area until the reign of Henry VII and retained the ownership of the mill.

In 1525 Robert Collyer was the owner of the mill and it remained in his family until John Heyman took it over at the beginning of the 18th century. On his death, the mill was left to his niece, Hannah Heyman, who made it over to her son by her first marriage, William Thompson, who later sold it to William Ryde. Ryde was in occupation in 1781 for, in July of that year, he insured his 'Brick, timber and tiled watermill' against fire damage. He died in 1786 leaving the freehold to his brother Thomas and then to Thomas's son, John. In 1827, John Ryde died and the property was left to his only daughter, Mary, who later married John Cooke, a Guildford grocer.

In 1830, Albury Mill was burnt down by James Warner, who was notorious as the last man hanged for arson in England and, although there had been a smaller fire at this mill in 1727, Warner's fire completely destroyed it. James Franks, the miller whom Warner shot at during the arson attack, ran the new mill built soon afterwards. In May 1910, the partnership between Henry Cooke and Charles Botting arranged at the turn of the century was dissolved, and, Botting constructed a new mill about one mile to the west.

Albury Mill has all the standard external features of a typical Victorian mill, and is constructed of four floors under a slate roof. It was powered by an overshot waterwheel and drove three pairs of stones although, at some later date, a turbine-driven roller system was installed.

The building is now used as an engineering testing laboratory, but all the machinery has been removed and the Tilling Bourne has been diverted away from the mill, to the north of the site.

ALBURY PARK MILL *Albury*
Tilling Bourne TQ 062479 — In Albury Park east of The Street.

This site now lies in open parkland but originally it formed part of an old village that disappeared under a major landscaping scheme carried out in the 19th century. A corn mill existed here in 1727 but in that year it was burnt to the ground. A new mill was built soon after, but was converted to a paper mill in 1795 by Charles Ball, who used it to print bank notes, but this was discontinued by 1811, and by 1839 the mill building had disappeared off the Tithe Map.

All traces of the mill have now completely disappeared, but the site can still be identified at a point where the Tilling Bourne divides by a small wooden weir.

BOWERS MILL *Burpham*
River Wey Navigation TQ 011529 — North of Clay Lane.

There is no documentary evidence to suggest that this was an ancient mill site and the first mention of a mill here was in 1733, when it was apparently a paper mill. There was also a corn mill, for in 1779 the occupier, Daniel Eaton, insured the contents of both paper and corn mills for £1000. Paper-making was discontinued soon after and in 1793 only corn was milled, by Benjamin and Richard Kidd.

On the First Edition of the Ordnance Survey map of 1816 the site is marked as an oil mill and it was also marked as such on Froggett's map of 1831.

It appears that linseed oil production ceased here soon after, since the site was recorded solely as a corn mill in 1831, in the occupation of Thomas Chandler. In the Tithe Apportionment of 1841, William Holden was the occupier followed by Thomas Peerless in 1845, John Holden in 1847, until Edward Childs took over in 1870, with the firm of Lintott & Sons continuing until 1877. Towards the end of the 19th century it was converted to a roller mill, by the milling firm of Messrs Ranger & Burrows. A trade magazine chronicles the change in machinery and records it as a 'Turner Roller System' installed in 1890 and powered by the extant breastshot waterwheel, 16ft in diameter by 12ft wide.

Messrs Ranger & Burrows were in control until 1899 after which the firm was renamed Ranger & Co, but by 1910 milling had ceased. The lease was advertised for sale but was never taken up.

A report on the state of the mill in 1932 recorded that it was timber-framed, rectangular and low, with brick up to the first floor, then weatherboarding under a tiled roof, and all in a state of disrepair. The mill building was demolished in 1945, the timber removed to the estate of the Duke of Sutherland, who lived at the nearby Sutton Place. The building now on the site was originally built as a laundry for Sutton Place but was eventually converted to a private house.

Water power was provided from the River Wey Navigation at a point just to the south of Bower's Lock. The lock gates bear the date 1933 and therefore it was probable that the mill race, and the other associated watercourses, were removed at the same time.

CASTLE MILL *Dorking*
River Mole TQ 179502 — Situated north of the Reigate Road.

The restoration of Castle Mill, by past RIBA president, the architect Michael Manser, earned a European Heritage Award in 1974 and, without the input here of a considerable amount of money, the mill by now would have fallen into complete disrepair, or collapsed altogether.

The present building stands on the site of a Domesday mill, but little is known about the early history of the site apart from the fact that in 1649 it formed part of the manor of West Betchworth and in 1760 belonged to the Betchworth Castle estate. George Dewdney took over the running of the mill in 1743 and by 1765 his son, James had taken out a further lease. By 1821, he had erected stables, outbuildings and a tenement, all at considerable cost to himself. On his death in 1827, his son, George, succeeded him, and it was he who carried out further improvements, the most notable of which was the enlargement completed in 1836. This involved the demolition of the single-storey structure attached to the mill and its replacement with a two-storey brick and weatherboarded extension.

The lease was taken over by Anne Franks in 1849 and she had two daughters, Lavinia and Louise. By 1861 Lavinia, aged 24, was the occupier and was recorded as a 'miller and farmer'. From 1862 until 1883 Henry Mills was the miller, at which time the lease was advertised in a trade magazine:

'To be let on a lease, a water corn mill driving 4-pairs of stones with convenient storerooms and other outbuildings, together with fifteen acres of very productive meadow land. An excellent residence and two cottages. On the River Mole with an unfailing supply of water. Present tenant has been in possession for twenty years and there is an extensive retail and grist trade.'

William Payne took over the lease at a rental of £150 per annum, but fifteen years later the occupier was recorded as William Clifton. On his death in 1905, the local corn and seed merchants, W. & H. Atkinson, took over. The Atkinsons continued to rent it until 1921 when, as Lot 41 of the Denbies Estate, the freehold was offered for sale and purchased by Henry Atkinson for £1,600.

Atkinson continued to employ the old carter, Tommy Alderman, and the miller, Joe Killick, both of whom had worked at the mill since the end of the 19th century. Alderman used to run flour to Kingston with a three-horse team starting out at 4am and returning home at 8pm, no doubt stopping on the way for suitable refreshment. After a fire in 1933 the mill continued on a much reduced scale, manufacturing animal feed in its latter working days when only one pair of the original four pairs of stones was used, together with an oat crusher and, in 1949, this pair of stones stopped working, the mill finally closing down in 1952.

When George Dewdney took over in 1829, apart from extending the mill building, he installed pit machinery and the waterwheel, which are still extant. This breastshot waterwheel is cast iron and 16ft 10in in diameter by 6ft 2in wide with three sets of eight arms on a cast iron octagonal axle shaft. By 1977 most of the wooden starts had rotted away along with most of the iron floats. Since then, the waterwheel has been completely refurbished, with 144 new wooden starts securing 48 paddle boards of elm. The primary drive machinery was of a standard layout with nothing out of the ordinary, apart from the fact that there was a different method of tentering for each pair of stones. The pit wheel, 10ft 6in in diameter, is constructed in iron, cast in halves with wooden teeth. The spur wheel is of cast iron, with wooden teeth but unusually, its outer rim is wooden and bolted together in six segments on to which the compass arms are bolted. The upright shaft was evidently cut from a pine tree and could possibly pre-date the installation of the cast-iron machinery. It is a massive piece of timber with its base set onto an inverted 'V' arch girder, located on brick pillars on the pit floor.

Castle Mill, without doubt, is one of Surrey's most important mills and is at the base of a small hill to the east of Dorking, and although it is no distance from the Reigate-Dorking road, it is completely hidden. Situated as it is, adjacent to the River Mole, water supply was never a problem, and at times during the winter months, it could be a real nuisance. Indeed, in the proceedings of the Institute of Civil Engineers of 1881, reference is made to a series of 'notches' cut into one of the posts of the mill to register flood levels. Most of the marks were said to be several feet above the average river level. A weir just upstream from the mill channelled the water *via* a leat to the waterwheel, and the only maintenance required was the constant clearance of debris from the mill race. The layout of the mill is L-shaped, with a mansard roof; that part of the mill adjacent to the river is the oldest.

After its closure in 1952 there was much discussion by Dorking Urban District Council as to how to preserve the mill. Permission for its use as a furniture store was refused but, as the mill was rapidly deteriorating, the Local Authority agreed to conversion for residential use.

In 1978 the owners decided to get the waterwheel working again, with the intention of driving a small generator. The idea was initially hampered because the mill race was choked up with mud and rubbish, and also by the Thames Water Authority, who had extensively regraded this part of the River Mole. As the River Authority had lowered the river level by five feet, the owners of the mill had to lower the mill race by a similar amount to get any flow of water to the wheel. The waterwheel that was originally breastshot became undershot!

There is no doubt that Castle Mill is an attractive and important Surrey watermill and, with the landscaped waterside gardens, it forms a pleasant scene. The waterwheel has been completed renovated by the existing owner and turns freely during the summer months.

CLANDON MILL *West Clandon*
Tributary to River Wey TQ 040519 — North of Clandon House.

It appears to have escaped most people's attention that there was a watermill at West Clandon. A public footpath leading east to west bisects Clandon Park, and the mill was sited beside it at a point below the lowest of two artificially constructed ponds.

In 1642, Sir Richard Weston, who was the instigator of the scheme to make the River Wey navigable from the Thames to Guildford, sold his land at Clandon to Richard Onslow. It is not known whether there was a mill on the site but, as Weston was a noted agriculturist, it may be assumed he would have the necessary ability to organise its construction. The first documentary reference to a mill here was in 1656, when it was let to Henry Hinley by Sir Arthur Onslow; it was described as 'A watermill at West Clandon'. In 1711 it was described rather grandly as 'Clandon Mills' in a tenancy agreement granted to John Glassington.

John Rocque's map of 1768 marks the exact position of the mill, below a circular pond that still exists today. After being marked as 'Merrow Mill' on Greenwood's map of 1823, all references to the mill disappear and it is not known when it ceased working or when it was demolished.

FETCHAM MILL *Fetcham*
Tributary to River Mole TQ 160563 — At the end of Mill Lane.

Fetcham Mill was the principal corn mill for Leatherhead and the surrounding area, until it was burnt down and destroyed by fire in 1917. The building stood on a site that was probably used at the time of the Domesday Survey. In 1293 a watermill was granted by Adam le Sousse to John D'Abernon and later, in 1514, a baillif's account of Sir Edmund Bray's manor of Fetcham included a watermill called 'Cutte Mill' which was let for £5 per annum. A much later agreement in 1705 between Francis Vincent and Arthur Moore made reference to 'A capital messuage and mansion house including a watermill in Fetcham called "Cutte Mill"'.

Little is known about the type of mill in existence at that time, as the only references record just owners and millers. The last mill to stand on the site was probably constructed during the late 18th century.

Thomas Withall was the miller until 1791, when Henry Ellis took over; then Henry and Horace, his two sons, born in 1805 and 1808 respectively, became millers in due course. Their partnership was dissolved in 1842 — Henry remained. After his death in 1849, the next recorded occupier was William Sturt, who stayed until 1887. The large milling firm of Henry Moore took over and ran the mill in conjunction with similar interests at Ockham and Cobham Mills.

On 2 August 1917 the mill caught fire and was destroyed, just leaving some brick walling. A photograph, taken at the turn of the century, shows it was a fairly large building, which apparently contained three pairs of stones. The mill was powered by an internally mounted iron overshot waterwheel, 12ft in diameter, that also drove a water pump for Baddington Hall.

By the end of March 1918 it was decided that none of the iron machinery, except the waterwheel, would be of any use if the mill was rebuilt. The machinery was sold to a scrap metal merchant for £5. The rusting frame of the waterwheel remained for many years, but even this has now gone. The large spring-fed millpond was used extensively for watercress growing by Messrs Mizen Bros until at least 1957, even though the Cobham end of the millpond had been filled in 1931.

FOREST GREEN MILL *Forest Green*
Tributary to River Arun TQ 119416 — At the end of Mill Lane north of Ockley Road.

Forest Green Mill was, until quite recently, just an empty building located north of the village of that name. The mill lies at the end of a private drive and is an undistinguished building of brick and slate with no architectural merit whatsoever, and its design suggests that it was built in the latter half of the 19th century. Its one positive attribute is that it stands below the slopes of Leith Hill in an area of outstanding natural beauty.

It was originally one of two mills working in the district, both isolated from the main watermilling areas of Surrey and, as with its neighbour, Oakwood Mill, it appears to be of relatively modern formation. The first reference to a mill here is on John Senex's map of 1729 and the first documentary record of occupation is revealed in 1832 when James Chandler, a miller late of Forest Green Mill, was made bankrupt. The next occupier was Mr E. Halls, but he was soon followed by Charles King in 1851. Along with his son, Mark, he also controlled Paddington Mill at Abinger, having taken over the tenancy there in 1845. King only stayed at Forest Green Mill for four years but he continued at Paddington Mill until 1895. Edward Coldman took over the tenancy from King and remained in occupation until 1882 but, surprisingly, no information appears to exist about him or his operation.

The local corn merchants, Weller Bros, then took over and ran it with their other watermill, Oakwood Mill, and with the windmill at Cranleigh. Under the control of Harry Weller, Forest Green Mill continued working until 1915, when it finally closed down.

After closure it lay empty, the machinery removed soon after. The once attractive and idyllic millpond, that had powered an overshot waterwheel, has been drained, adding to the air of gloom.

It is puzzling that such a mill was built here, using materials so out of context with the surrounding countryside. The mill is almost square in shape, built totally of brick of three floors under a slate roof, perhaps because of its close proximity to several local brickyards.

The site and the former mill building have recently been purchased by a school, which has converted it to a field studies centre.

GOMSHALL MILL *Gomshall*
Tilling Bourne TQ 085478 — Adjacent to Station Road (A25)

There has been a watermill on this site at Gomshall certainly since before 1086. Undoubtedly, it was the most important building of its kind in the area and survived all of the other flour mills on the Tilling Bourne.

The existing mill building is timber-framed and brick built, parts of it dating to the 17th century. It was then that expansion took place and the Tilling Bourne was dammed to form a millpond. In 1611 the mill was leased by Edward Bray to John Chennel for £16 per year, and in the mid-18th century, when still in the ownership of the Bray family, it was leased to David Harris of Shere. Until 1828 the mill was in the ownership of Richard Simmons and in September of that year it was advertised for sale.

The mill was purchased by William Southorn, a local man, who owned a bakery in Shere. It was advertised again on 26 March 1850, as part of the estate of the late William Southorn. The mill was sold to Benjamin Kelsey, who ran it, Leigh Mill and the nearby Netley Mill until his death in 1877, after which his son Richard took over. The mill was again up for sale in 1884. It was not sold, for two years later a partnership between Ann and Richard Kelsey was dissolved, the outstanding debts paid by Richard Kelsey, who continued at the mill. It was finally sold in 1897 to George Egerton who installed his two nephews as tenants. Gomshall Mill continued working commercially until its closure in 1953.

Gomshall Mill is unusual if not unique for, when the mill was last extended, no consideration was given to installing an upright shaft. This decision led to a low, two-storey watermill, which contained layshaft drives from two waterwheels, working side by side from the Tilling Bourne, which runs through the centre of the mill. Prior to 1839, the mill was powered by one waterwheel, but this was replaced with two internal overshot wheels, one of which was removed for scrap, like many others, in 1939. A 10hp Hornsby engine was installed to replace the lost power after its removal.

After closure, the mill lay derelict until 1964, when it was purchased by the present owners, who converted it to a restaurant and antique shop while retaining the waterwheel and drive machinery. There were plans to pull the mill down in the late 1940s while it was still operating but, due to the foresight of someone unknown, it was saved.

Gomshall Mill, with its most unusual appearance, set across the Tilling Bourne, is a pleasant survival.

MILTON COURT MILL *Westcott*
Pippbrook TQ 150492 — At the end of the access road to Milton Court.

The last watermill to stand on this site was pulled down in about 1947 and was, by all accounts, a large and interesting building, of a design far removed from the more standard layouts commonly found throughout the county.

The mill was built entirely of wood, which in itself is unusual and, although it is first shown on John Senex's map of 1729, there are strong indications that this is an ancient mill site. It is situated within the grounds of the Jacobean manor house, Milton Court, a listed building that dates back to 1611. This house was built by Richard Evelyn and is said to have replaced an earlier building, and the estate would have included a watermill. The mill took its name from the house; it is recorded as Milton Court Mill on most documents.

The mill demolished after the last war only dated from about 1860, and replaced a smaller wooden one which had a clasp arm overshot waterwheel. The new mill had an unusually decorative tiled roof, with three gables, together with other distinctive and unusual woodwork. The fact that it was entirely constructed of wood probably led to its demise through disrepair, and unfortunately, little is known about the drive machinery apart from the fact that it contained three pairs of stones. Photographs show that the externally mounted overshot waterwheel was quite large.

Thomas Wells was the recorded occupier and the mill remained in the same family, with John, and finally Alfred, who was made bankrupt in 1879. The estate was then in the ownership of L.M. Rake and the mill continued working until 31 March 1900, under the control of Mr Black, the last working miller. It lay derelict until it was dismantled for its timber. Like Hedgecourt Mill near Felbridge, Milton Court Mill was an important watermill in terms of industrial rural architecture, and a sad loss.

The mill site is easily located, as the mill cottage still remains. On the opposite side of the road embankment lies the millpond, now inevitably choked with weeds: Milton Court Mill has become another of the 'lost' watermills of Surrey.

NETLEY MILL *Gomshall*
Tilling Bourne TQ 079479 — South of Station Road.

Netley Mill is a short distance downstream from Gomshall Mill but, unlike its more prestigious neighbour, was irregularly used. There are several references to Netley Mill being disused and empty and not having worked for some time.

This undoubtedly is an old mill site for, in 1233, a mill here belonged to the Abbey of Netley, by Southampton Water, which is how it got its name. Unlike the more distinguished and functional watermills on the Tilling Bourne, Netley Mill was certainly the exception in the architectural sense, with its square ruined tower and pointed window arches, reminiscent of the Gothic period. The 'ruined' section of the upper part of the mill has all the external appearance of a folly, which it was when the surviving mill building was built towards the end of the 18th century.

Edward Lomax was the person responsible and he concluded an unusual financial arrangement whereby he retained half the profits of the business when he leased the mill. Throughout his life Lomax certainly did not conform and his ideas on estate management were also far different from the accepted practices of the time.

As Netley Mill was so near Gomshall Mill, it was inevitable that the ownership of both sites, and in some cases the miller, would be the same, especially during the 19th century. Both mills were in the ownership of William Southorn until his death in 1850, after which his widow took over the running of the mill and the estate. It appears that Benjamin Kelsey took over the mill and continued until 1877, after which Arthur Franks became the occupier until 1907, when the mill ceased working.

Netley Mill is built mostly in brick, while at the back of the mill coursed rubble stonework is evident. The existing mill was originally fitted with a large breastshot waterwheel, but in due course this was replaced with a more efficient wheel of the overshot variety.

Some years after closure the site was purchased by the Hurtwood Water Co, who used the building as a pumping station, and the mill house for accommodation. In 1970 house and mill were for sale, and were bought by the owner of Gomshall Mill, thus recreating the partnership between the two.

OAKWOOD MILL *Ockley*

Standon Brook TQ 136383 — Located west of Stane Street.

This is one of two watermills in the countryside near Ockley but, unlike its neighbour, Forest Green Mill, no traces remain of the building itself.

This is not an old mill site, and records suggest that only one mill ever stood here. The first reference appears on John Senex's map of 1729 and, from a photograph of the building in the Guildford Museum, the external appearance confirms an 18th century origin. On closer inspection the western bay of the building may well have been the original mill, and the mill was probably extended to increase its storage capacity. The external waterwheel was subsequently enclosed. The original building had a half-hipped roof, while the extension possessed a mansard roof with leaded light windows. Inside, the waterwheel was 17ft in diameter by 5ft 6in wide and, apart from the iron floats, was constructed entirely of wood, the mill containing three pairs of stones.

Oakwood Mill was on the Standon Brook, a tributary of the River Arun and, to accommodate the rather irregular flow of water, an extensive water-ponding arrangement was introduced. An earth dam was constructed across the stream, just to the north of the mill. A millpond was then formed almost 300 yards long and between 20 and 50 yards in width. An overflow causeway ran the whole length of the pond, so that excess water could be quickly cleared.

Richard Tidy was the miller in 1845 while James Humphrey had taken over by 1870 and stayed until 1899. After he had gone, local corn merchants Weller Bros took over and ran the mill until 1913. Closure soon followed, no doubt due to the water supply and the ageing machinery.

The mill was finally pulled down in 1945, the materials used for repairing wooden farm buildings. All that remains now are traces of the millpond, odd fragments of brickwork and the memory of Oakwood Mill.

PADDINGTON MILL *Abinger*

Tilling Bourne TQ 100472 — Adjacent to Guildford Road, east of Abinger Hammer.

Paddington Mill takes its name from the nearby 15th century farm, but there are earlier documented references. In 1305 it is mentioned in connection with Adam de Gurney and was worth 13s 6d.

Charles and Mark King were in occupation from 1845, although it seems their business partnership was dissolved soon after. However, both father and son remained at the mill until 1870, after which Mark King became the sole occupier and stayed on until 1895. The mill was then taken over by the local watercress firm, R. & J. Coe, who carried on for another twenty years; then it was used for storage. The Water Resources Survey of 1851 records that the mill contained two pairs of stones and produced, on average, forty sacks of flour per week.

The building itself is rather unattractive but is typical of the early Victorian period. Nevertheless, it is in picturesque surroundings, though the once large millpond no longer exists. The mill had an overshot waterwheel, 10ft in diameter, but this was dismantled for scrap many years ago. The wheel shaft remains *in situ* and is constructed in iron with a diameter of 9in which, unusually, tapers down at each end. Above this, on the iron pentrough, appears the name 'Tom Spence Millwright of Guildford' along with, in bolder letters, 'W.J. Evelyn 1867', accompanied by monograms on either side.

The inside of this brick-built mill is empty, with a general air of decay, and the structural state of the building must be in some doubt.

PARSONAGE MILL *Dorking*
Pippbrook TQ 161497 — Located west of Station Road.

Until this mill was demolished in 1959, it was one of Surrey's oldest watermills, and was of such an unusual shape and size that it defied any standard building design. Perhaps storage space was most important here and the random building extensions were erected for productivity and efficiency, but certainly throughout Surrey there was never a mill to match it. The top floor, for instance, was partly in the adjoining mill house and it seems that the layout of the interior floors complemented the jumbled external appearance of the mill. It was white painted with brick to the first floor, three floors above, and weatherboarding above that, under a slate roof.

The last mill to occupy the site was erected in 1702 and from 1859, and probably earlier, it remained in the tenancy of the same family up to the sale of the Denbies estate in September 1921. Mr E.A. Attlee purchased the freehold of this mill and, at the same time, closed down Pixham Mill, used by him since 1882.

To complement the old watermill, a purpose-built roller mill was erected at right angles to it in 1900 and eventually this led to the closure of the older mill in 1950. In the name of progress this fine mill was pulled down in 1959 and replaced by a 'modern' one, that in turn caused the roller mill to shut down, but this brick-built mill is still extant today and used for storage.

This mill site is still 'active' now, but no flour milling is carried out, as the modern machinery produces cattle, pig and poultry food. The millpond has inevitably been drained and filled in but the Pippbrook still meanders through the site, which is one hundred yards south-east of Dorking Town railway station.

PIPPBROOK MILL *Dorking*
Pippbrook TQ 169499 — Adjacent to Old London Road.

This is a rectangular, brick-built building with a slate roof, which stands on an 11th century site. There are two extraordinary features about the mill, that may not be apparent to the casual observer: firstly, the existing mill dates from 1979, and secondly, it was a double mill with machinery both sides of the spillway.

The last working watermill on this site dates from the end of the 18th century; it finally ceased working in 1932. On 6 December 1979 that mill caught fire and burnt for six hours before the Fire Brigade brought the blaze under control. The mill was completely gutted with only the brick flank walls surviving but, as it was a listed building, it was rebuilt exactly in its original form. Unlike the disastrous fire of 1979, that of 1882 was not so catastrophic and prompt action by the Dorking Volunteer Fire Brigade saved the mill.

For many years the mill was in the ownership of the Denbies estate, and one of the most pleasant features associated with it is the large and attractive millpond, now part of a recreational area known as Meadowbank. This millpond is clearly marked on the 1649 estate map, although the mill is not shown. The unusual machinery of the former mill merits comment, as there were two separate 'systems' in operation here, making Pippbrook a six pair mill altogether. The spillway rushes through the centre of the mill, and the bisected northern section machinery was powered by an external overshot waterwheel. The cast iron wheel and pentrough were installed here in 1840, manufactured by J. Booth & Sons of Congleton to a diameter of 10ft and width 8ft 6in, but this fine wheel was removed for scrap in 1940.

Various millers used the mill during the 19th century, but before that, in 1797, it was let to Thomas Turner. John Abel was the miller in 1845, followed by Joseph and Alfred Ede until 1883. Henry and Albert Joyce then worked here for the next ten years until Trower Bros took over. The Denbies estate was up for sale in 1921, and Pippbrook Mill was listed in the sale particulars under the tenancy of Herbert Jay & Co Ltd. A Mr Aggs purchased the freehold of mill and cottage and, on his death in 1932, the mill was again up for sale, with a strong possibility of demolition. Although it ceased production that year, the mill remained and the millpond was donated to the Local Authority for the benefit of the community.

During the last war the mill was utilised as an AFS station and afterwards, as a furniture upholsterers, which it remained for many years. In 1977, an inspection of the pit floor in the southern half of the mill was carried out by the author and various pieces of cast iron machinery were still *in situ*. The earth floor was in poor condition and was reputed to contain a well shaft of unending depth, which made further inspection out of the question!

This was never the most attractive watermill in Surrey, but its location and solid construction added style to a building all but lost in 1979.

PIXHAM MILL *Dorking*
Pippbrook TQ 174507 — On the west side of Pixham Lane

When Jack Hillier visited Pixham Mill in the 1940s, he dismissed the mill as 'of late date and barely within my scope'. This is rather harsh as the existing mill building was erected in 1837 and replaced an earlier mill that, until at least 1826, was being leased by Messrs Joseph and John Sanders. The builders of the new mill in 1837 did not bother with fancy brickwork but built to a rectangular floor plan with three floors of brickwork under a pitched roof designed for the storage of 500 quarters of corn. The external overshot waterwheel, 13ft in diameter by 10ft wide, was constructed in iron but only the axle shaft and some of its compass arms now remain.

James Dewdney was the recorded occupant and still resident when the mill was advertised for sale:

'To be sold by auction. Flour mill rebuilt in 1837, four stories high. Best machinery being alternate wood and iron throughout. The waterwheel is overshot 13ft in diameter by 10ft wide, with iron shaft driving 4-pairs of stones and a flour machine. Stream has fall of 16'. Capable of grinding between 100-170 quarters of wheat per week. A double cottage adjoins the mill. Also there is a detached residence.'

Dewdney continued as the miller here after the sale, now probably as the owner until 1874, after which William Slade took over. Slade did not stay long for, by 1878, he had left and was working as the miller at Coxes Lock Mill near Weybridge. The next occupant was Edwin Challen and the mill was advertised for sale in 1881. The freehold was purchased by John and William Attlee, who used the mill to supplement their other watermill, Parsonage Mill, which was on the other side of Dorking. They were certainly still in occupation in 1905, but at what time Pixham Mill ceased working is not clear, as trade directories show its use as a corn merchants until 1922. The internal drive machinery was removed in 1937 and installed in a watermill in Sussex.

Once the mill was empty the natural use of the building was that of a warehouse and, during the last war, Moss Bros used it to store military uniforms. In delightful surroundings, with extensive views of Box Hill, the building has now been converted to a private house.

ROOKERY MILLS *Westcott*
Pippbrook TQ 132481 & TQ 132479 — Adjacent to Rookery Drive south west of Westcott.

The Rookery estate was purchased in 1759 by David Malthus, father of famous economist Thomas Malthus. Malthus built a large mansion here, alas now gone, and landscaped the surrounding grounds which then included two large lakes.

There were two watermills on the estate before 1759 as both are marked on John Senex's map of 1729 as 'Westgate Mills'. One was on the embankment between the lakes, while the other was below the lower lake; both were primarily flour mills.

In 1851 the Water Resources Survey states that the owner of the estate, including the two mills, was Mr R. Fuller and they were both statute mills, working alternately, both containing two pairs of stones that produced a combined average total of forty sacks of flour per week.

George Bird was the tenant of the Lower Mill in 1805 and by 1856 Joseph Rose was the recorded occupier. The Upper Mill was shown as a saw mill on the 1st Edition of the 1/2500 Ordnance Survey map of 1869, while earlier, in 1866, all trade references to the Upper Mill cease. The Lower Mill building was still extant in 1924, for it is included in the sale particulars of the Rookery estate.

All traces of Upper Mill have gone but the Lower Mill was converted to a private dwelling in 1945, although the former mill building was virtually rebuilt.

The mill sites are near to a private road in an area still known today as The Rookery, although the mansion has been replaced by a block of luxury flats.

WESTCOTT MILL *Westcott*
Pippbrook TQ 137487 — At the end of a drive leading off Westcott Street.

The mill at Westcott is undoubtedly that recorded in the Domesday Survey and valued at 30d. As it was close to the source of the Pippbrook, it must have suffered in early times from a lack of water, particularly in the summer months. To overcome this, a large millpond was constructed in the 17th century with a total surface area of six acres, to an overall depth of ten feet.

The existing mill building was erected in about 1850, rectangular in shape and built of brick under a slate roof. James Bravery was the miller here at the time of a fire in 1843, and it must have proved too much, for he died of shock two weeks later. Thomas Killick was the tenant of the new mill, and he remained until 1878. In 1851 the Water Resources Survey records that the mill contained three pairs of stones, and produced, on average, 55 sacks of flour per week with an annual turnover of £416. The partnership of King and King took over the tenancy but in 1882 that was dissolved. Edward Wilcox was the next occupier and continued until 1895, and after he left, Charles Hall took over until 1904. No details exist as to the type of machinery, but from a measurement of the wheelpit the waterwheel must have been overshot and at least 15ft in diameter.

Westcott Mill finally ceased working in 1909, with the machinery sold for scrap in 1912. By then, the empty mill was in the ownership of Mr Brooke, who also owned the famous tea company, and he utilised the building as a fishing lodge, for the millpond was a 'roach fishing paradise'. The former mill has been converted to a house of some style but the water still cascades into the wheelpit.

OTHER CENTRAL SURREY WATERMILL SITES

Botting's Mill (TQ 039480)
This mill was erected by Charles Botting, following the dissolution of his partnership with Henry Cooke, at Albury Mill in 1910. It was originally turbine driven and continued in work until February 1990, producing mainly animal feed, using electricity. In the early years of the 19th century a mill on this site was used for paper-making under the direction of Sir William Magnay, and this mill continued working until about 1876.

Chilworth Mill (TQ 025475)
The complex mill site at Chilworth was used for corn milling, gunpowder production and paper-making, utilising the Tilling Bourne which flows through the site. Gunpowder production ceased in 1920, while the paper mill, adjacent to Blacksmith Lane, was destroyed by fire in 1896.

Friday Street Mill (TQ 128455)
The large millpond is all that remains of this former mill site that certainly powered a corn mill in 1579. This site, on the Tilling Bourne, was closed down in 1736.

Upper Postford Mill (TQ 041480)
This was a paper mill in the ownership of Charles Ball at the beginning of the 19th century. It was recorded as disused in 1830 and demolished some years later.

Two other unnamed water-powered mill sites in Central Surrey were: a paper mill near Chilworth marked as 'New Mill' on the Tithe map of 1846, although it is recorded as unoccupied (TQ 039476), (certainly in use in 1865 but not mentioned in 1871; it ended its days as a sawmill driven by a turbine, and building and turbine still remain), and a paper mill on the River Wey at Send (TQ 022531), marked as such on John Senex's map of 1729.

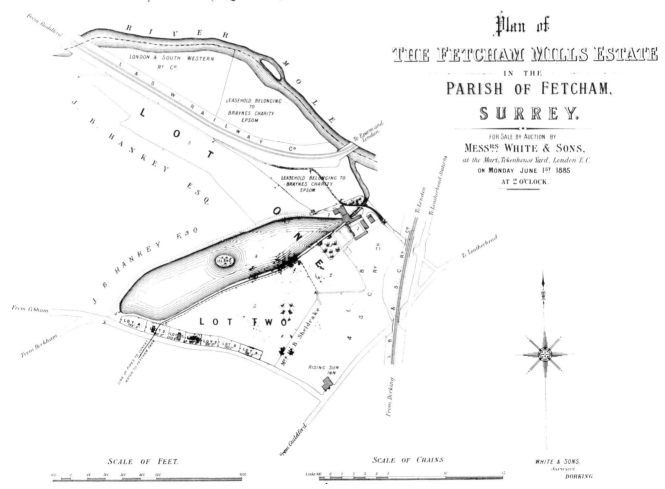

60

OPPOSITE: A sale notice of Fetcham Mill in 1885; (DK) ABOVE: A
photograph in 1906, and BELOW: fire was a constant hazard at any mill,
and this was certainly true here in 1917. (JS)

LEFT: Rookery Upper Mill almost lost in vegetation (JA) and BELOW:
Rookery Lower Mill in 1907. RIGHT: A traditional photographic scene
at Westcott Mill at the turn of the century. BELOW: Parsonage Mill was
certainly a building with a haphazard building construction.

ABOVE: Castle Mill, 1885. BELOW: The view looking down to Castle
Mill in 1905. (JA)

ABOVE: Castle Mill in 1905, revealing a large group of buildings;
LEFT: a close up view of the wheel side about 1930 (DN) and RIGHT:
dereliction in 1970. (MM)

LEFT: The restored Castle Mill won a European Heritage Award in 1974. (SPD) RIGHT: Pixham Mill in May 1941 when it was used as a warehouse. (RCHME) BELOW: Pippbrook Mill just before the turn of the century. (DK)

ABOVE: Gomshall Mill, 1885. BELOW: Gomshall Mill at the turn of century.

Milton Court Mill, 1885.

ABOVE: Netley Mill in 1912, clearly showing that part of the mill built as a folly. BELOW: Albury Mill was a typical Victorian mill building. (JS) OPPOSITE ABOVE: Bottings Mill was erected in 1910 and was turbine driven. CENTRE LEFT: The small and rather insignificant Paddington Mill photographed in 1979. RIGHT: Forest Green Mill has recently been converted into a Field Studies Centre. The large millpond was drained many years ago. BELOW: The ancient Oakwood Mill, lying derelict in 1920.

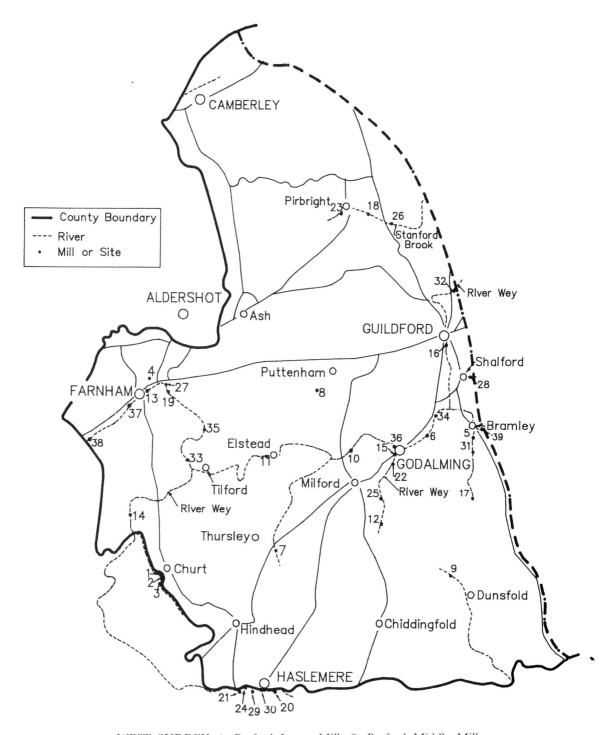

WEST SURREY: 1. Barford Lower Mill, 2. Barford Middle Mill, 3. Barford Upper Mill, 4. Bourne Mill, 5. Bramley Mill, 6. Catteshall Mill, 7. Cosford Mill, 8. Cutt Mill, 9. Dunsfold Mill, 10. Eashing Mill, 11. Elstead Mill, 12. Enton Mill, 13. Farnham Hatch Mill, 14. Frensham Mill, 15. Godalming Hatch Mill, 16. Guildford Town Mill, 17. Hascombe Mill, 18. Heath Mill, 19. High Mill, 20. Lowder Mill, 21. New Mill, 22. Ockford Mill, 23. Pirbright Mill, 24. Pitfold Mill, 25. Rake Mill, 26. Rickford Mill, 27. Rock Mill, 28. Shalford Mill, 29. Shottermill, 30. Sickle Mill, 31. Snowdenham Mill, 32. Stoke Mill, 33. Tilford Mill, 34. Unstead Mill, 35. Waverley Mill, 36. Westbrook Mill, 37. Weydon Mill, 38. Willey Mill, 39. Wonersh Mill.

THE MILLS OF WEST SURREY

BARFORD MIDDLE MILL *Churt*

Tributary to River Wey SU 854378 — Adjacent to a track that leads off Kitts Lane.

Unlike the Upper and Lower Mills at Churt, this site was never associated with the paper-making industry.

Henry Pain was the miller in 1799, while later in 1847 N. Fuller was the owner-occupier. The Water Resources Survey of 1851 states that it was a two pair mill with a plentiful supply of water. A directory entry gives W. Chalcroft as the miller in 1882, while he was followed by Samuel Croucher, who was still the miller when the wheel axle shaft broke in 1914 and the mill closed down.

The idyllic location lent itself to the inevitable house conversion but the mill was demolished and replaced by a house, possibly using some of the original materials. The millpond has been reduced in size, and access to the site is prohibited, but a right of way passes close by.

BOURNE MILL *Farnham*

Tributary to River Wey SU 852474 — Adjacent to Guildford Road, north-east of town centre.

Bourne Mill was not powered by the River Wey, even though the river passed close by. Small streams that issue in Farnham Park were of sufficient capacity to supply water to power the mill and to fill a reasonably large millpond. The existing mill building dates back to the 17th century and was no doubt the last of several to occupy the site.

The Simmonds family took over in 1808 with Thomas as the first miller. William Simmonds took over in about 1845 and he in turn left it to his son Alfred, who was the last working miller.

There are numerous references to Bourne Mill in the 19th century, and in 1849 the mill was valued by Charles Osborne on behalf of the owner of the site, the Bishop of Winchester:

'Bourne Mill, the property of the Bishop of Winchester and granted on a lease to William Simmonds. Annual value £110. Old mill (not used) £7. The buildings are very old and warrant considerable repair. The mill is overshot with two waterwheels and has a fair supply of water. The old mill is very slightly built of wood and has not been used for many years. There is but little fall between it and Bourne Mill, and injures the mill more than its value.'

The mill was put up for sale in 1906 owing to the retirement of Alfred Simmonds, but whether it was sold is unknown; later, in 1924, a public enquiry was convened to consider the proposed purchase by Farnham UDC along with thirty-five acres of land. The Council wanted to buy it so that the Guildford Road could be widened but the Board of Guardians opposed on the grounds that the mill had been in existence for 300 years and other land could be used. The outcome of the public enquiry can be seen today. The front of the mill has been partially demolished and the front face of the mill now rises like a steep cliff five storeys high. Modern windows have been installed and the facade is supported by four incongruous stepped buttresses.

Part of the mill is now let to various craft and woodwork tenants, but the adjoining mill house, of later date, serves as an antique shop. An inscription 'TM 1751' is on the outside of a small brick-built structure, possibly a 'miller's convenience', set across the by-pass stream, which obviously refers to Thomas Matchwich, owner of the mill at the time.

Bourne Mill is a fascinating jumble of red brickwork and weatherboarding built in a mixture of styles, and is one of the oldest remaining mill buildings to be found in Surrey. Behind it is a large millpond, idyllic as ever.

BRAMLEY MILL *Bramley*
Tributary to River Wey TQ 006447 — In Mill Lane, west of the High Street.

Unlike its neighbour, Snowdenham Mill, just upstream, this is a much older mill site. In 1295 Gilbert le Colvene, of Hednescumbe, granted a lease for life to Joan Karrington for a messuage including a fulling mill. The first reference to a corn mill appears in 1687 while, later in the same century, a lease was granted to Jasper Shrubb.

Nothing further appears until 1851 when Samuel Hooper was the miller. By 1862 John Andrews had taken over and it remained in the same family until 1914, with Albert and then Charles taking over in later years. It was a three pair mill capable of producing 55 sacks of flour per week, and the high output could well be attributed to the extensive millpond. Corn merchants D. Taylor & Son took over in 1915 and ran the mill in conjunction with their other concern at Rickford Mill.

Bramley Mill had ceased working by 1931, and in 1935 it was converted to a house, the machinery removed for scrap. The former watermill and the attached 17th century mill house form a most attractive group of buildings, and the millpond has become a haven for wildlife.

CATTESHALL MILL *Godalming*
River Wey SU 983443 — Adjacent to Catteshall Lane.

Catteshall Mill was one of six watermills in the Godalming area and, down the years, the site has housed a variety of industrial processes — corn milling, fulling, leather-dressing and paper-making. All these industries utilized the water power of the River Wey, which passes through the site.

Catteshall was undoubtedly one of the three mills credited to Godalming in the Domesday Survey. In 1391 the site accommodated a fulling mill, but also in that year reference is made to a corn mill, both of which were in the control of the Laneway family. Later on, as wool-related industries declined, so corn milling increased at this site and developed into a major business.

Henry Moline was the last corn miller at Catteshall Mill and, when he moved to Unstead Mill in 1845, corn milling ceased here. Paper-making and leather-dressing then became the principal industries.

Although waterwheels had been used extensively, from 1869 a Fourneyron water turbine was installed to power the paper-making machinery. This turbine was manufactured by MacAdam Bros of Belfast and is thought to be one of the largest of its type ever built. To the credit of the members of the Surrey Industrial History Group, the turbine, a scheduled Ancient Monument, was removed prior to demolition of the former paper-mill buildings. It will be displayed at a site by the River Wey in Godalming at some time in the future.

COSFORD MILL *Thursley*
Tributary to River Wey SU 913396 — Adjacent to a farm track east of Thursley.

Cosford Mill is an exceptional watermill; parts of the building date back to the 15th century and it contains some of the oldest machinery to be found in Surrey. The mill was for many years under the control and ownership of Cosford House, hence its name, until the freehold of the site was sold to the present owners in 1952. A small stream that rises in Witley Forest has been ponded artificially at four locations upstream, with Cosford Mill set below the lowest pond.

Originally, it was a one pair mill, but extensive alterations were made at the beginning of the 18th century, which included the rebuilding of the mill, improved accommodation for the miller and an extra pair of millstones. The mill is constructed on four floors, mostly of brick and Bargate stone, and is set at right angles to the attached mill cottage, which is of two floors.

The mill had an overshot waterwheel which succumbed to the demand for iron in the last war, and now only the stub end of the 6in diameter cast iron axle shaft remains. Inside the mill most of the machinery remains *in situ*, some of it of considerable age, especially the pit gearing, with the pit wheel itself of 7ft 6in diameter and of the clasp arm variety. This wheel turned a cast-iron wallower, affixed to the massive wooden upright shaft, which rests rather precariously on a horizontal timber, laid between the hurstings on the pit floor. Set above the wallower, on the upright shaft, is a truly superb example of a wooden clasp arm spur wheel of 11ft 6in diameter. This wheel drove two stone nuts which were lifted out of gear by jack rings. A well-worn ladder leads to the stone floor above, where there are two pairs of french burr stones, both 42in in diameter. Also there are the remains of a flour grader and a cast iron crown wheel of 4ft 4in diameter, while on the floor above there are four grain bins. Loading the wheat into the mill, and the flour out, took little time, for a door from the top floor leads directly onto the causeway of the pond embankment at the back of the mill.

A trade directory registers that Henry Pope was the miller here in 1845, with Henry Denyer taking over in 1855. Denyer stayed at the mill until 1888 from which date Richard Budd took over; when the mill ceased working he moved on to High Salvington windmill in West Sussex. Budd was responsible for installing a new waterwheel during his stay at Cosford Mill; it was made by a foundry in Reading.

In 1952 the freehold was sold. The site was totally engulfed in a mass of vegetation, with mature tress growing inside and outside the mill. After two years of hard work the mill was habitable, and to such a high standard that it was featured in the magazine *Homes and Gardens* in 1959. Situated as it is below a pond embankment, flooding was at times a problem. In the floods of 1968, the highest of the four ponds burst its banks, flooding the mill to a depth of five feet. The force of the water buckled the cast-iron window frames facing the millpond on the ground floor.

CUTT MILL *Puttenham*
Tributary to River Wey SU 914456 — At the end of Cuttmill Lane.

A small stream which rises near Seale forms a chain of five substantial ponds that divide Hampton Park and Puttenham Common. The lowest of these is known as The Tarn and it is from this expanse of water that power was derived to drive Cutt Mill.

This is an ancient mill site that has seen a succession of watermills, the last of which ceased working in the 1930s. A mill is mentioned here in 1307 when it was given by John de Cotte to John le Paumer as a marriage portion for his daughter Juliana. At the end of the 16th century the mill was already part of the Puttenham Priory estate, and later it appeared in the estate records of Hampton Lodge.

In 1768 the estate was offered for sale by the owner, Thomas Parker, and sale items included a 'complete watermill, much under let to Mr Bicknell for £53 per annum, on a lease which expires in 1792'. In 1822 the mill formed part of the settlement when Edward Long married Lady Walpole of nearby Rodsall Manor.

Little is known about the last Cutt Mill, the only references being to some of the millers operating here during the 19th century such as James Hale (1845–1874) and Edward Durrant (1874–1898), who was also using Rake Mill, near Milford, from 1862.

The mill stood in the grounds of Cutt Mill House, a grand building dating from the 17th century. A small brick and stone building, now used as a garage, is all that remains of the mill itself. The waterwheel was removed in 1932, and the water now falls from the pond and cascades down into an ornamental rockery, where three french burr stones are displayed.

DUNSFOLD MILL *Dunsfold*
Tributary to River Arun TQ 001361 — Adjacent to Church Green.

This mill site certainly dates back to 1580, when a George Austin was recorded as the owner of 'two mills' at Dunsfold. Throughout the ensuing years, until the 17th century, there are only vague references to 'Dunsfold Mills' while the existing mill site is shown on Norden's map of 1594 and later on all the large scale maps of the county. It is about three quarters of a mile west of the village at a point where the river runs along the edge of Dunsfold Common. Next door is the parish church, which dates to the 13th century and, as both sites are rather detached from the present village centre, this suggests a previous settlement.

In 1755 Dunsfold Mill formed part of an inventory of properties for sale or rent in the area, and later, William Bowers was the miller. William Lassam, a farmer and miller, occupied the mill in 1851, then in 1866 Sarah Lassam was the tenant, after which Thomas Wonham took over. Wonham remained there until 1878, Weller Bros taking over until 1909, after which the mill is not recorded.

A photograph at the turn of the century shows it to be entirely of wood, under a tiled roof, with an enclosed waterwheel. Dunsfold Mill was demolished many years ago and only the footings of the wheel pit can be seen today.

EASHING MILL *Eashing*
River Wey SU 946438 — Adjacent to Eashing Road.

The use of water power at this site was similar to that of Stoke Mill, Guildford, in that both corn milling and paper-making were carried out together.

The first reference to Eashing Mill appears in 1658 when the corn mill was conveyed to William West. As he was a paper-maker it could be assumed that he was responsible for introducing the industry at Eashing Mill, but no reference to a proprietor is recorded. Thomas Hall bequeathed to his wife the rents of his corn and paper mills in 1704 and his family and descendants continued in occupation until 1779, according to a fire insurance entry. The following year both mills were in the possession of Richard Smith but in 1826 he was made bankrupt. A report by paper-makers Messrs Pewtress & Co in 1865 makes reference to their mill building being in existence for thirty years. They were also using Stoke Mill to prepare pulp for paper-making at Eashing Mill.

The erection of the new mill marked the end of corn milling and over the ensuing years Eashing Mill became an important site for paper production, while later in 1895 it was used by the Mitcham Wool Co. Turbines eventually replaced the waterwheels, but these were removed when an engineering firm took over.

Eashing Mill is set in a delightful corner of Surrey, south-east of the village of Eashing, and the approach from the village is by way of the old Eashing Bridge, a classified Ancient Monument.

ELSTEAD MILL *Elstead*
River Wey SU 903438 — Adjacent to the Farnham–Milford Road.

Pevsner described Elstead Mill as the finest of its kind in Surrey, and most people who have seen the mill would agree. It is a tall and handsome building of red brick with a tiled roof, surmounted by an ornate cupola, of classical design.

As with the ancient mill sites in Farnham, it belonged to the Bishop of Winchester and reference to this site appears on the rent rolls of 1208. It was a corn mill then, and the occupier was Osbert the miller. In 1610 the mill was owned by Laurence Elliot of Godalming, with Hugh Moth as lessee and miller. The site was later described as 'a corn mill, malt mill and a fulling mill with one little house and yard', but in 1647 the mill burnt down.

There are numerous references to the owners and occupiers during the 17th and 18th centuries: 1675–Henry Tribe to John Budgeon, 1676–Phyllis Tribe to John Tice, 1692–John Garton of Ifield Mill, Sussex, 1694–William Garton to his son John, 1694–John Garton to Richard Lutman, 1718–Joseph Tice to John Rogers, 1728–Joseph Tice to Joseph Smythe, 1757–Joseph Smythe, miller, 1777–William Hogflesh to Richard Keen. By the middle of the 19th century, Henry Appleton & Sons were using the mill as a worsted fringe factory, but by 1878 the business had become unprofitable and the mill was closed down.

The mill has now been completely gutted and is used only for storage. Although it was described as a woollen mill during its last working days, a close inspection of the inside revealed that it also housed a corn mill. This trade was accommodated within the main mill building, and was powered by an undershot waterwheel positioned in the massive wheel race. At the southern end of the mill, positioned on the outside wall and now covered by brick and weatherboarded extension, is an iron undershot waterwheel with L-shaped buckets which are fixed to the rim by wooden starts. The diameter of this wheel is 15ft by 5ft wide. The waterwheel was subsequently used to generate electricity for the mill house until 1948. Until quite recently, Elstead Mill was a private house, but now it has been converted to a restaurant.

ENTON MILL *Witley*
Tributary to River Wey SU 950400 — At the end of Mill Lane

Enton Mill is located to the east of the village of Witley and, although the mill building remains intact, it has been incorporated in the wing of a modern dwelling, and it is difficult to assess its external appearance as an operational watermill. The mill took its name from nearby Enton Hall, in whose ownership it remained for some considerable time.

This is certainly an old mill site and the miller's cottage, attached to the east side of the mill, is reputed to date back to the 15th century.

In 1781 this, and the nearby Rake Mill were owned by John Chandler, with Thomas Munton the miller at Enton Mill. Eighteen years later the mill was owned by the trustees of John Hall, who had been a paper-maker at Eashing Mill. Previously he had insured the contents of Eashing Mill and Enton Mill for £600 each. John Lasham is the recorded miller here in 1805 while four years later Richard Snelling was the proprietor. From 1838 the mill was in the occupation of the Whitbourn family, with Thomas taking over from Richard in 1859 and he in turn leaving it to Arthur in 1867. Arthur Whitbourn continued as miller until closure in 1899.

In its latter working days the mill contained three pairs of stones and, together with the mill cottage, it was valued at £924 in the Water Resources Survey of 1851. Following the conversion of the mill at the turn of the century, the sturdy wooden upright shaft was retained and now forms the central support pillar for a spiral staircase.

Enton Mill is set amid a series of lakes and assorted woodland and, despite the nearby London–Portsmouth railway line, enjoys one of the most attractive settings in Surrey.

FARNHAM HATCH MILL *Farnham*

River Wey (North Branch) SU 846470 — Adjacent to Farnham by-pass.

Although early references to this site are rather scarce, in 1231 monks from the nearby Waverley Abbey were using a fulling mill on the site, and were also granted a right of way from the 'great water meadows' to the village centre. By 1691, a corn mill was in existence according to a lease issued by the owner, the Bishop of Winchester.

John Stanton was the recorded miller in 1722, and later, in 1798 John Pisely surrendered his old lease of 1773 for a new one. His son Joseph carried on the business until 1832. John Darvill then took over the mill and it remained in his family until 1870. At some time, one of the Darvill family, probably John, purchased the freehold from the Bishop. A Land Tax Assessment of 1859 refers to James Darvill as owner and occupier of 'Bishop's Mill', Farnham. Before the Farnham by-pass was built, access to the site was by way of a track leading north-east from the junction of South Street and Abbey Street, and on the Ordnance Survey map of 1913 this track is noted as Darvill's Lane. Henry Rose purchased the mill from James Darvill and it remained in his ownership until 1889, after which the mill and the surrounding land were acquired by Mr E. Bide, who used the building as a dairy and as a firewood factory. Just after the turn of the century, the building was used as a laundry, and remained as such until 1962. The River Wey, which used to run through it, was diverted soon after corn milling ceased and now the mill stands alone in open ground.

The former mill building was purchased in 1962 by Farnham UDC at a total cost of £17,000 and was converted to a civil defence centre. After this, the premises were rented by a motor oil firm, with the mill building itself used as an Arts Centre, while at the moment it is used as the rehearsal studios for the local Redgrave Theatre.

Hatch Mill is an attractive building constructed on three floors of red brick, with a delightful lunetted door at its eastern end. This part of the building is the original mill and, with the adjoining mill house, dates from the 18th century. At some time during the following century, the mill was enlarged, though a map of Farnham surveyed by William Harding in 1839 showed the original mill.

The size and external appearance of Hatch Mill is similar to that of Guildford Town Mill and, although the mill does not contain any machinery, it is an interesting industrial building relating to a period when Farnham was an important market town.

FRENSHAM MILL *Frensham*

River Wey (South Branch) SU 837410 — Junction of Pitt Lane and The Street.

The sandy heathland and pine trees that make up Frensham Common are complemented by two ponds, the largest of which is called the Great Pond, situated on the south-west of the common. Indirectly, the outlet from this pond, feeding from a surface area of approximately 200 acres, entered the River Wey just above Frensham Mill, thus ensuring that the mill was never short of water even though the main river flows through the site.

Although Frensham Mill is first shown on John Rocque's map of 1768, this is an ancient mill site dating back to at least 1217 when the mill at 'Feresham' is mentioned in the Bishop of Winchester's Rent Rolls. Later references record that John Giles was the miller in 1739, while Richard Beale was here in 1800, and it remained in the same family until its closure. Although Richard Beale was the recorded miller in 1800 his father Thomas was still in charge of the business side. On his death, Richard took control until 1855, from which date he left the mill to his three sons, Richard, John and Benjamin, with the former as miller.

In 1876 the existing three pair mill was demolished and replaced by a much larger building and at the same time the stone bridge, at the front of the mill, was constructed to improve access. Richard Beale, the oldest son, remained as the miller until he retired and handed over control to his son, also Richard. He, together with his brother Edgar, continued in partnership until the last years of the 19th century and in 1894 the mill was let to Edgar Beale's son-in-law, William Milsun, who was the last miller at this site.

An article in a trade magazine of 1896 relates that the newly installed two sack roller system, manufactured by Henry Simon of Manchester, was worked by a breastshot waterwheel 15ft in diameter.

The mill finally ceased working in 1920, but the reason for its closure is unknown. A photograph of 1906 shows that this was a most substantial mill, possibly the largest in south-west Surrey. It was constructed entirely of brick on four floors under a tiled roof, and would certainly have lasted for many years if it had not been demolished. Sadly this took place in 1922 and the millrace, which passed through the centre of the mill, has now been covered by timber; all that remains is the mill house and a fine three storey granary.

GODALMING HATCH MILL *Godalming*
Tributary to River Wey SU 966438 — Adjacent to Mill Lane.

Hatch Mill is to the west of Godalming High Street, and the building is a substantial one, with sections dating back to the 17th century. This is most probably one of the three Domesday mill sites credited to the town, as there are early references relating specifically to Hatch Mill. The water supply was plentiful and storage was improved with the construction of a large millpond behind the mill, and maximum efficiency achieved from the large overshot waterwheel.

In 1483 John Guy, the miller, was prosecuted for taking excessive toll. In 1599 a lease was granted to William and John Wonham by John Elliot. Thomas Hall was the miller in 1712 when the mill was in the ownership of John Westbrook, a family no doubt connected with the large industrial complex to the north-west of Hatch Mill. In 1792 John Roker was the owner with Benjamin Kidd the miller. Ownership of the mill remained in the Roker family until 1882. When Benjamin Kidd died in 1800 his sons Benjamin and Richard succeeded as tenants until 1826. Thomas Oliver, a mealman from Haslemere, took over the tenancy in 1826 at a rental of £125 per annum. After a period of occupation by the Allden brothers between 1890 and 1905, control passed to the well-known and established firm of J.C. Withers. When the once-plentiful supply of water started to decrease the firm installed a water turbine, manufactured by Gilbert Gilkes & Gordon Ltd of Kendal, in May 1940, and the opportunity was taken to install some modern machinery. Milling ceased here in 1950, but the firm continued in occupation as agricultural merchants, using the mill for storage, until its closure in 1965. Since then, the buildings have provided further storage facilities for a light industrial firm.

The mill itself is constructed in two distinct sections, with the portion fronting Mill Lane of later date than the rest. Unusually, part of this building is supported on wooden piles with the river flowing underneath, while the original mill is a patchwork of brick and timber under a tiled roof. Two dormer windows, lead lighted, provide a reasonable amount of illumination to the seventeen meal bins, an indication of the variety and quantity of the work carried out. Although the mill is devoid of machinery, the water turbine has survived *in situ*, next to the north-west side of the building.

GUILDFORD TOWN MILL *Guildford*
River Wey SU 996492 — Adjacent to Millbrook.

There is no watermill recorded for Guildford in the Domesday Survey even though, by then, the town was of a substantial size and population. However, it is improbable that the town did not possess one.

The existing site dates back to at least 1295, when Walter de la Poyle excavated a leat for the River Wey to power a mill. Originally this site no doubt contained a fulling mill in accordance with Guildford's prominent position in the woollen trade. With the decline of this industry in the middle of the 17th century corn milling became the principal trade, although a limited amount of fulling was still carried out on some part of the site.

A lease issued to Roger Valler in 1707 gives an indication of the layout of the mill(s) of that time. A dwelling house was attached to the mill and a separate outbuilding for grading flour was erected between the corn and fulling mills. There were four pairs of stones, two for flour production and two for grinding provender food. An illustration by the Guildford artist John Russell in the mid-17th century shows a ramshackle line of dilapidated buildings with three external waterwheels. These were probably the same mills referred to in the 1707 lease. It is easy to appreciate the importance of this mill site, apart from Guildford's prominence as a market town. Earlier in 1653 the Wey Navigation was opened and immediately made the transfer of wheat and flour a viable proposition. Flooding was a problem at the site, and by 1768 the old mill buildings had become rather dilapidated, partly due to flood damage. The eastern section was demolished and rebuilt in brick, while the western section, known as the 'Hogsmeat Mill', was just repaired.

Two important changes also took place in 1768 to improve efficiency. Firstly, the level of the Navigation was raised to improve the head of water and secondly, the more efficient breastshot waterwheels were installed. Further improvements to the fabric of the mill were made in 1827 and 1852, when the old 'Hogsmeat Mill' was demolished and a new building attached to the existing mill, built to the same size and style to match that of 1770. Following the 1827 alterations the lease was put up for sale and, perhaps for the first time, a detailed description was recorded. The lease was divided into three lots. Lot 1 was the eastern part of the mill and contained two pairs of stones and was capable of grinding 18 loads of wheat per week; Lot 2 was the remaining half of the building and it also contained two pairs of stones. The remaining lot was the 'Hogsmeat Mill' to the west, and apparently in the occupation of Mr W. Elkins. It was also mentioned that the mill was attached to the Guildford Foundry, but by 1852 this mill was reported as demolished.

The 19th century saw a great expansion in the corn/milling industry especially so after the repeal of the Corn Laws in 1846. The Town Mill was no exception and particularly from the 1870s, foreign wheat could literally be shipped to the front door, and it would have been a common sight to see London-based barges unloading and loading here. However, as rapidly as the upsurge in corn-milling began, its demise was as dramatic.

With the advent of the roller mills, even large watermills, such as the Town Mill with its traditional machinery, had great difficulty in competing economically. Surprisingly, the owners of the Town Mill did not install the new roller milling machinery, as surely the mill could have easily accommodated such a system. Whether the miller or mill owners thought that they could compete with the roller mills is unknown, but the refusal to update and convert the existing machinery resulted in closure in 1892.

The Town Mill had a succession of different millers throughout the 18th and 19th centuries, working in the two separate businesses, as opposed to many mills where members of the same family continued for many years. In 1781 Gabriel Ryde insured the contents of his mill against fire damage for £500, confirming the importance of the mill even at that time. Charles Booker took over the mill from Ryde in 1787, and in a new lease of 1791, the mill was said to contain six pairs of stones (both mills being included). After the spell of occupation by Mr W. Elkins, Benjamin Kidd was the miller. Finally, the mill came under the control of the Chitty family, with Edward responsible for the erection of the new buildings of 1852. John Chitty took over in 1874 and he was followed by William Chitty in 1887.

This mill, devoid of any machinery, is now used as a scenery workshop for the adjacent Yvonne Arnaud Theatre.

HASCOMBE MILL *Hascombe*
Tributary to River Wey TQ 000400 — On east side of Godalming Road.

The skeleton of the watermill and some stone footings are the only remains of Hascombe Mill. The overshot waterwheel, 16ft in diameter by 3ft wide, is now devoid of any buckets and lies partially submerged in thick undergrowth; it is constructed of iron and set on a wooden axle shaft.

Hascombe Mill certainly dates back to 1690, when it was marked on John Seller's map. It formed part of a freehold estate put up for sale in 1819, and later that year the tenancy was taken up by John Lambert at a rental of £23 per annum. The mill was described as: 'An overshot water corn mill with 2-pairs of stones, store room, tenement annex, kitchen and bakehouse.'

By 1845 Francis Philpott was the miller, and later in 1856, James Purdey was recorded as an insolvent debtor 'late of Hascombe Mill'. The tenancy changed hands frequently: 1866–Robert Durrant, 1882–Albert and Henry Harris, 1887-1890–William Bicknell. In 1851 the Water Resources Survey revealed that Thomas Durrant was the miller (and at Rake Mill) and that the mill worked on average five hours daily, grinding and producing twenty-three sacks of flour per week.

Being near the source of the stream, a millpond had to be constructed, and the Survey records that in 1851 the mill was only working part time. It ceased working in the late 1890s.

HEATH MILL *Worplesdon*
Hodge Brook SU 960549 — In Heath Mill Lane leading off Guildford Road.

Heath Mill is a brick-built building that has been converted to a private house. It has the distinction of being the most recently built of Surrey's watermills, erected in 1902. Jack Hillier describes it rather scathingly as a sentry box. True, the mill has all the external appearances of a typical Victorian industrial building, but the yellow brickwork offsets the harshness of the building line rather nicely.

This does not appear to be an ancient mill site, although there is a brief reference to a mill in this area, possibly Heath, during the reign of Henry VIII, but the mill is certainly shown on Senex's map of 1729. James Horner was the proprietor to at least 1832 and James Reville was the next recorded miller in 1866. By 1870 John Sherman had taken control with his son, Thomas, finally taking over until the mill was destroyed by fire in 1900. In 1898 the lease of the mill was advertised: 'To be let, a water corn mill, 4 miles from Guildford. 3 pairs stones, silks etc doing a good flour and retail trade.'

After a brief occupation by John Hamilton, James Bailey was the next miller and he remained until 1922. Mr H. Jones took over and continued to produce stoneground flour using the existing french burr stones. At a time when watermills were producing white flour from foreign wheat, Heath Mill stood alone and became known as the 'Heath Health Mill', until final closure in the 1950s.

The original mill, before its destruction by fire in 1900, contained three pairs of stones and was capable of producing on average fifty sacks of flour per week.

The waterwheel and the pit machinery are still *in situ* and the externally mounted waterwheel is overshot. Regrettably, this fine example of an overshot wheel of 12ft 4in diameter by 6ft 10in wide is virtually devoid of buckets and rusting away. The iron pentrough, that channelled the water to the top of the wheel, is unusually shallow and the penstock bears the inscription 'Weyman and Hitchcock — Engineers — Guildford 1895'. The pit machinery is modern, of course, having been installed with the new mill. The iron pit wheel is of 10ft diameter with wooden teeth, while the wallower is all iron and 2ft 9in in diameter, and likewise the spur wheel of 8ft 2in diameter. The pit machinery is carried on a 6ft square iron upright shaft, whose base bearing is set in a metal plate supported at each end by brick piers.

A high embankment was constructed here to pond the small tributary that flows through the site but the present owners of the mill, and the River Authority, have carried out extensive drainage work to prevent flooding, and the large millpond is no more.

HIGH MILL *Farnham*
River Wey (North Branch) SU 857472 — Situated on a track off Moor Park Lane east of Farnham.

High Mill is an important Surrey watermill which contains pit machinery of some considerable age as well as an undershot waterwheel.

In 1288 William Blyas, a corn miller, was evicted from the mill and fined 20s, which was a considerable sum at the time, but nothing further is known until 1692 when a fulling mill is mentioned. For centuries the ownership of the site, along with other Farnham mills, lay with the Bishop of Winchester. References are made in 1776 and 1819 respectively, to Charles Bacon and Nicholas Bacon as tenants, although the latter refers to a corn mill that was formerly a fulling mill. William Cowdery was the next miller, with his son Charles taking over in 1839. The mill ceased grinding commercially in about 1900 and thereafter only produced provender food, when in the ownership of Edward Bide, who also owned an horticultural nursery in the town. Mr Hide was the miller until his death in 1940, having worked at High Mill for the previous twenty years. Mr Whale took over and produced provender food to feed the many horses owned by Mr Bide. He also used a recently installed saw bench, for which purpose the waterwheel was primarily used, until final closure in 1950.

The lack of historical references to High Mill is more than balanced by the unusual arrangement and age of the pit machinery. The mill is unique in the county, and probably elsewhere, for its primary drive machinery, where the pit wheel is keyed to the end of the waterwheel shaft and drives the wallower from 'outside'. The wheel shaft passes under a wooden beam resting on the sides of the hursting, which also supports the upright shaft. The pit wheel and the spur wheel are wooden and of the clasp-arm type of construction, being 7ft and 6ft in diameter respectively. The wallower is also wooden and is 3ft in diameter and complemented by a wooden upright shaft of 13in diameter. Although the existing machinery originally drove two pairs of stones, one set has been removed and the area where it was located has been planked over. The upright shaft projects 6ft above the stone floor and carries a 4ft diameter cast-iron crown wheel with wooden teeth, and this engaged a cast-iron pinion which drove a long pulley driveshaft, extending twenty feet in a line parallel with the front of the mill, and then a further ten feet into the adjacent bay. A variety of ancillary machinery was driven by this shafting, including the sack hoist, which was operated by the jockey control method. Also on the stone floor is a circular wooden tun with vertically planked sides, surrounding a bedstone of unknown thickness and a 9in thick runner stone of 48in diameter and apparently french burrs. On the bin floor are the remains of three large grain hoppers with a central walkway, and the whole area formed a short bay over the milling area of the floor below.

The internal waterwheel is undershot, 12ft in diameter by 3ft wide, and is positioned in one of the three brick channels that run the whole width of the mill. The wheel is constructed in cast iron with thirty-two wooden paddle boards. A bypass channel exists about one hundred yards upstream of the mill, presumably as a safeguard in times of flood or excessive flow in the river. The area of land around the mill is shown as 'liable to flood' on the large scale maps of the area.

For such a large mill it is rather surprising that it only contained two pairs of stones but, as there is only a 2' head of water here, it is doubtful that the waterwheel could exceed 10 hp. However, there is evidence of a second waterwheel, positioned in the third water channel, with the assumption that another two pairs of stones existed at the opposite end of the mill. It is more likely that the waterwheel was used to power fulling machinery.

High Mill is constructed to the first floor in brick with tarred weatherboarding above, all under a tiled, half-hipped roof and, although the mill is well away from a public road, a footpath passes the front door.

LOWDER MILL *Haslemere*
Tributary to River Wey SU 900316 — Adjacent to Lowder Mill Road.

This mill is first shown on John Senex's map of 1729 and there is no evidence of an older mill. As it was situated on a small tributary of the River Wey, water supply must always have been a problem. To combat this, two pen ponds, plus a millpond, were constructed using ingenious earthwork excavation. Each of the pen ponds are on the side of a hill, with an embankment supporting the lower side. The Water Resources Survey of 1851 gives the proprietor as J. Lucas, and the mill is described as 'Flour and Grist', and containing two pairs of stones. The mill worked on average ten hours a day, which is itself not surprising considering the amount of stored water, and produced 40 sacks of flour per week.

Little is known about it from 1851 and it is also not known when grinding ceased, although no miller is mentioned in the 1881 census. By 1939, the waterwheel and associated machinery had been removed but the mill building survived. It is constructed of stone with some brick infilling, under a tiled roof and is of three storeys, but of no distinctive style. The mill is hidden away behind the small, but attractive, mill house, and technically the whole site lies in West Sussex, with the county boundary with Surrey mered to the by-pass stream to the north of the mill.

NEW MILL *Shottermill*
Tributary to River Wey SU 885324 — South of Critchmere Lane.

This was the most westerly of the Haslemere Mills and today, although the site has not been redeveloped, it is difficult to identify the position of the mill and the once expansive millpond. A variety of trades were carried out here, in what was a paper mill, a flour mill and a skin mill.

In 1801 it was known as Hall's Mill, after the resident paper-maker, and it clearly remained in the same trade for some time with Pewtress, Low and Pewtress here in 1839 and James Simmonds in 1846. The Water Resources Survey of 1851 shows that the mill contained 'Two Paper Engines'. A directory entry in 1878 records that Edward Dunce 'a miller, grocer and postmaster' was in occupation, and on the Ordnance Survey map published in 1873, the site is marked 'flour'. By 1882, Edwin Masters, a tanner, deer, buff and chamois leather-dresser, was using it in conjunction with the nearby Pitfold Mill. This trade ceased before the turn of the century, and the mill was described as derelict in 1902.

The mill building was geographically in West Sussex, the county boundary with Surrey being adjacent to the northern bank of the millpond. The site was used as a pig farm, and later in 1930 the millpond was filled in. In 1978 a new sewage plant was constructed next to the site, which led to the demolition of the mill and of its associated buildings. All that can be seen today is a flat and uncultivated piece of land.

OCKFORD MILL *Godalming*
Tributary to River Wey SU 962433 — Adjacent to the Portsmouth Road, south west of Godalming.

Even before it was converted from corn milling to storage, Ockford Mill was never the most attractive of Surrey's watermills. Its dark coloured brickwork, design and construction, suggest it dates from the early 19th century.

The first recorded miller was John Peacock, who lived here between 1835 and 1844. Richard and William Sisely used the mill until 1882 in conjunction with their other business interest at Unstead Mill. Later, in 1882, Samuel Shole was the miller and he continued to at least 1887. Francis Ashby came next and, along with his other interest at Gomshall Mill, initially ran a profitable business. However, in 1905 he went into partnership with George Cole, for financial reasons, but two years later, Cole was running the mill on his own. The final occupants of the working mill were the well-known corn merchants, J.C. Withers, who were also using Hatch Mill in the centre of Godalming, where they continued after the closure of Ockford Mill in 1934.

At some time a turbine had been installed to replace the waterwheel, although the large millpond at the rear of the mill must have provided an ample supply of water. After closure the machinery was removed and the premises taken over by the Heald Sack Company. The former mill building has been extensively modernised and, although the name Ockford Mill has been retained, the present building bears little resemblance to a watermill.

PIRBRIGHT MILL *Pirbright*
Stanford Brook SU 942554 — Adjacent to Mill Lane north west of village.

This mill forms part of an attractive group of buildings, set between the mill house and a large granary. All three buildings are partly below the embankment of a large millpond, now drained and devoid of any standing water.

The earliest documentary reference to a mill is on Senex's map of 1729 and, because of its close proximity to the 16th century Manor House, the mill was known at times as the 'Manor Mill'. The mill house displays a stone tablet dated 1780, but the mill is probably later. Nonetheless, the massive support timbers for the pit and stone floor are of considerable age.

John and Thomas Woods were the recorded millers here at the end of the 18th century, and after them a succession of millers worked here: 1839–Mr Harding, 1852–Thomas Leftwich, 1870–William Leftwich, 1905–Frederick Gurr, 1909–James Gurr, 1915–John Gurr. The mill ceased in 1939 with a local farmer, Mr Hetherington, as occupier. It had also been used for sawing wood for in 1851, the mill was capable of sawing 5,000 feet of timber per week.

Unusually for a Surrey watermill, most of the machinery remains and is of a common type. What is different here is that the wooden upright shaft is set upon a large, and seemingly cumbersome, 4ft high cast-iron arch, while the top of the shaft rests in bearings suspended from brackets 6ft above the stone floor. Also on the stone floor are some pencilled inscriptions to be found on a wooden support beam; 'Two new stone nuts 1889', 'New stones May 20 1875', 'New crown wheel 1892'. The waterwheel is mounted within the mill and was, until quite recently, little more than a skeleton constructed in iron, and overshot, with a diameter of 11ft 1in and a width of 6ft. Attached to the rim of this wheel were small metal plates inscribed

'Brooks and Shoobridge — Guildford'. Most of the machinery inside is relatively modern, apart from the wooden spur wheel of 7ft diameter. The pit wheel is iron and 10ft in diameter while the crown wheel is 3ft 10in in diameter, with the mill containing three pairs of stones.

Until a few years ago, small but distinctive cracks adorned the front wall of the mill and the wooden interior was slowly rotting away. However, new owners have carried out extensive renovations and the mill has been converted to residential accommodation, with most of the machinery retained, along with the waterwheel, which has been rebuilt.

RAKE MILL *Witley*
Tributary to River Wey SU 951412 — Adjacent to Rake Lane.

There is now just a small pond here within the grounds of Rake House, on a higher level than the road that passes close by. This is an old mill site for there are references to it in 1576, when Robert Mellershe was recorded as holding a fulling mill, called 'Rakes Mill', in Witley, together with twenty acres of land.

Following the decline of the wool industry, the fulling mill was replaced with a corn mill by 1676. John Woods was the miller in 1785 and several years later he insured it for £400, and after for £450 in 1805. In 1829 a new corn mill was erected, in the occupation of Thomas Woods. Thomas Durrant was the tenant in 1845, and in that year part of the large millpond was taken by the London–Portsmouth railway for the construction of an embankment. The Water Resources Survey of 1851 confirms Durrant as the miller, and that the mill contained three pairs of stones with the machinery in good condition; there were 33 acres of land. Edward Durrant was there in 1862 and stayed until the mill ceased working in 1895. It burnt down in 1903, and shortly after, a dynamo was installed on the site to produce electricity by means of a turbine manufactured by J.J. Armfield & Co of Ringwood. There is little to be seen on the site today except for the remains of the water turbine embedded in the wall of the dam.

RICKFORD MILL *Worplesdon*
Stanford Brook SU 965546 — Adjacent to the Guildford Road.

Rickford Mill has been converted to a house of some distinction, although most of the internal machinery was scrapped when the mill ceased working. The mill is located on the south bank of the Stanford Brook, a tributary of the River Wey, and is almost next to the Guildford to Bagshot Road, from which it is screened by weeping willows and larch trees.

The mill is built of brick of four floors under a tiled roof, with the top-storey brickwork covered unusually at each end with tarred weatherboarding. The building dates from the late 18th century and replaced the original mill.

The first documented reference appears in a sale advertisement in 1833, when the mill contained three pairs of stoncs. After the sale there were a succession of millers: 1846–James Franks, 1851–R. Jarrett, 1859–Henry Ede (also at Shellwood Windmill), 1866–William Foster, 1882–John Wonham, 1887–A.E. Youngs & Co and finally, D. Taylor & Son (also at Bramley Mill). Mr Arthur Chuter was the last miller to use Rickford Mill under the direction of D. Taylor & Son. When the Taylors took over in 1915 they were using Bramley Mill, but it ceased working in 1931, after which they concentrated their corn milling at Rickford until its closure in 1959. In its final working days only provender food was produced.

In 1906 the waterwheel was replaced by a 25in 'British Empire' turbine manufactured by J.J. Armfield & Co of Ringwood. A drive shaft from the turbine carried a metal pinion which meshed directly through the wall to the old spur wheel inside the mill, thereby acting like a traditional stone nut. This spur wheel is of 10ft 6in diameter, compass armed, and constructed entirely of wood with hornbeam cogs.

On the first floor of the mill is a slightly raised wooden staging in which sits a peak millstone and, positioned on its edge beside it, is a runner stone of 46in diameter, both of which are sickle dressed. Adjacent to the millstones, and fitted to the pine upright shaft, is the iron compass-arm crown wheel, with upward-facing teeth. The upright shaft itself is of 18in diameter and rests on a bearing set into the base of the pit floor.

An interesting episode took place in July 1952 when Armfields, the manufacturer of the turbine, were called in to investigate its malfunction. Apparently, the vertical drive shaft from the turbine had somehow dropped, which caused the drive pinion to sit down hard on the gap in the mill wall, thus making the whole milling system inoperable.

After the closure of the mill in 1959 it lay derelict and partly gutted, but in 1966 it was converted to a private dwelling.

ROCK MILL *Farnham*
Tributary to River Wey SU 857472 — Located adjacent to a track leading to Moor Park.

Only the massive brick foundations remain to mark the position of what was once a powerful watermill. Rock Mill does not stand on an ancient mill site but was in the grounds of Rock House, the family home of the Simmonds family, who were prolific millers and corn merchants in the Farnham area. The house was built in 1770 and the mill was probably erected at the same time. In 1832 William Mellerish was the miller, no doubt an employee of the Simmonds, Thomas Simmonds himself took over by 1845. His son, also Thomas, succeeded his father and by then the mill was steam assisted.

The mill closed down in 1877, with Richard Simmonds the last owner, and the first attempt to sell it took place later that year. The sale notice makes reference to five pairs of stones driven by a 10hp Corliss engine; it was sold for £1200, and later on, in September, Richard Simmonds inserted the following notice in the *Surrey and Hants News*: 'Richard Simmonds begs to inform his customers, and the general public, that he has removed his business from Rock Mill to the new steam flour mills at Albert Road, Aldershot, on Monday 17th September and that orders addressed to him will receive his prompt and best attention'.

The water which originally used to drive the mill still tumbles down through the site from the gardens of Rock House, and it is clearly visible from the track that leads to Moor Park.

SHALFORD MILL *Shalford*
Tilling Bourne TQ 001476 — Situated east of The Street.

This is a four-storey 18th century watermill now preserved and maintained by the National Trust. The timber-framed building stands complete with its machinery, a rarity in Surrey and, although it is a 'static' mill, it is kept in an excellent state of repair.

The mill is brick-built to the first floor, then timber-framed above in chestnut and oak, with hung tiles almost down to the ground at the front of the mill, with weatherboarding at the rear.

The iron-framed waterwheel is internally mounted and is near the front door. The wheel, 13ft 6in in diameter by 7ft 6in wide, is of the low breastshot variety. On the other side of the brick partition wall from the waterwheel is a 9ft 6in diameter iron pit wheel with wooden cogs. The massive wooden upright shaft drives a magnificent spur wheel constructed in wood and 9ft in diameter, a truly exceptional piece of carpentry. Of the three pairs of stones originally contained in the mill, only one pair is complete, while only the bedstones remain of the other two. The third floor contains other ancillary machinery such as wire machines, oat crushers and the sack hoist. The corn bins on the top floor extend throughout the whole length of the mill, and still retain a highly polished surface imparted by the falling grain.

This is an ancient mill site for in 1332 the manor of East Shalford held one mill, while later, in 1547, Christopher Moore of Loseley owned a mill which had previously belonged to Robert Wintershall. By the middle of the 18th century, the mill was in the possession of John Mildred, and in 1753 the existing one was built, the date shown in his will. In 1794 Robert Austin was the owner, for in that year he leased it to Robert Howard, and later in 1806, to John Sparks. The Lambert family were tenants from 1832 until at least 1878, with the mill finally closing down in 1914, after which it rapidly fell into disrepair.

The mill was saved and given to the National Trust in 1932 by a mysterious group of people known as 'Ferguson's Gang'. The members of this group were dedicated to preserving various buildings around the country and then donating them to the Trust. No one knew the identities of the members, and at various times large sums of money were deposited at the Trust's headquarters to finance the preservation of selected buildings, such as Shalford Mill.

SHOTTERMILL *Haslemere*
Tributary to River Wey SU 882324 — Adjacent to Shottermill Road.

Until its final closure in 1939, Shottermill was one of the last working watermills in the area, but since the closure it has been converted to a house. The mill, and its two feeder ponds, are just in West Sussex.

There are suggestions that this site was used as an iron mill and for paper-making but this is doubtful. It was certainly a flour mill in 1826 with William Oliver in occupation, and remained in the occupation of the same family until it ceased working. Also the windmill at Grayswood was used by the Olivers until it was demolished in 1886. The Water Resources Survey of 1851 records that the mill only contained two pairs of stones.

Major improvements took place in 1880 when the overshot waterwheel, 14ft in diameter by 7ft 6in wide, was replaced by a 'Little Giant' water turbine at a cost of £50. The installation was carried out by William Tomsett, who operated from the Ockford Works at Godalming.

At the sale of the mill in 1939, the two millponds were purchased by the Haslemere Preservation Society, which later donated them to the National Trust. The mill is constructed in typical Victorian fashion, with yellow brickwork under a tiled roof. A weatherboarded lean-to at the southern end of the building marks the former position of the waterwheel and the replacement turbine.

SICKLE MILL *Haslemere*
Tributary to River Wey SU 888325 — Adjacent to New Road.

In 1735, this site belonged to James Simmonds, who was a paper-maker, while later in 1769, he insured a paper mill and corn mill here.

In 1854 the mill was sold to Henry and Thomas Appleton, who continued to make tissue paper to at least 1884, after which the buildings were converted to a military braid factory. Candle wicks for Prices' Candles were produced here in 1920, but shortly after that the Avamore Engineering Co, later the Avamore Pump Co, were in occupation, until 1930. The main body of the mill was then used as a council highways depôt, which it remains.

The mill house is of 17th century origin and is attached to the mill building but unfortunately, the front facade of the house has been rendered and is now rather nondescript. The one large millpond, at the back of the mill, has been drained and recently filled in with household refuse. A Gilkes turbine, installed in 1937, is still *in situ*.

SNOWDENHAM MILL *Bramley*

Tributary to River Wey TQ 001441 —. East of Snowdenham Lane, south west of Bramley.

Snowdenham Mill is a three-storeyed corn mill, built into the side of the substantial dam of a large millpond, and contains most of its machinery. A narrow private track runs along the top of the pond embankment and the door to the mill is at this level. This is not an ancient mill site and probably only dates back to the late 17th century; it is shown on Senex's map of 1729.

The existing mill building was seemingly constructed in three separate stages. The oldest section is of ironstone garneting and this was followed by a red-coloured brickwork, while the whole of the waterwheel end of the mill has been rebuilt in a later red brick. This work has the appearance of being carried out in the third quarter of the 19th century, whereas the main structure of the mill is probably 18th century with some parts even earlier. The mill was powered by the extant iron overshot waterwheel, 12ft 6in in diameter by 6ft 7in wide, with the water channelled to the wheel through the pond embankment by a large cast-iron trough. Unfortunately, time has not favoured the waterwheel as most of the buckets have rusted away. Traces also remain of an iron shield fixed over the top of the waterwheel, ahead of the pentrough that enable water to leave the pond *via* the trough without attention. Inside the mill most of the machinery remains and, although originally a three pair mill, the middle pair of stones has been removed together with its stone nut and spindle. The upstream stone nut is wooden and is fixed to a flat iron spindle, driving burr millstones of 46in diameter. The downstream millstones are also burrs of 45in diameter, with the runner stone bearing the inscription 'Hughes and Son'.

The 8ft 6in diameter cast-iron pit wheel, with beech cogs, engaged a cast-iron wallower, that has been blocked up out of gear, while above is the 7ft diameter cast-iron spur wheel, also fitted with beech cogs. The typically massive upright shaft is of pine and terminates in a bearing on the soffit of the stone floor above the 4ft 6in diameter iron crown wheel with beech cogs. The sack hoist was operated from a slack belt drive from a layshaft, with further belts taken off this to operate the surviving bolters and wire machines. The sack hoist drum with its compass-arm wooden pulley, now badly worn, is also constructed in pine.

The first recorded occupier of a mill here was James Stilwell, who insured his corn mill 'stoned and tiled' for £200 in May 1792. Joseph Head was the miller in 1851, with J. Roker taking over in 1862. Following the sale of the estate in 1879 the tenancy changed for in that year the miller was Albert Rothwell. Corn milling ceased but it was apparently grinding provender food in the 1930s, using the burr stones. A water pump was installed on the opposite side of the waterwheel in the 1890s, with the necessary drive through a small iron spur wheel fitted to the bearing side of the waterwheel.

Snowdenham Mill is just one of the few remaining watermills in Surrey still containing its machinery and is ripe for restoration. In 1979 the Committee of the Surrey Industrial History Group foresaw the possibility of restoring Snowdenham Mill back to full working order, but permission was eventually denied.

A recent inspection (1989) revealed that the whole mill building has further deteriorated. The mill stands neglected and open to the weather with the upper windows either missing or broken.

STOKE MILL *Guildford*
River Wey SU 998511 — Adjacent to the Woking Road.

In 1635 a mill was erected on this site by Sir Richard Weston. The first mention of a corn mill appears in a document of 1740 which refers to John Russell, a former mealman of Stoke Mill, being made bankrupt. The site also contained both a paper mill and a corn mill until 1869, when paper-making finally ceased production. No doubt the closure of paper-making was hastened by the fire of 1863, which totally destroyed the three storey wooden building. The insurance money was used to construct another paper mill which included a 25hp high pressure beam engine, manufactured by Filmer and Mason, but the venture failed within six years. In 1782 there was also a saw mill on the site.

Jasper Franks was the tenant in 1842 while John Holden was the miller until 1847, after which he moved to the nearby Bower's Mill at Burpham. The new lease was advertised in 1848: 'To be let on a lease for a term not exceeding 14 years. Stoke Mill, working three pairs of stones, situate on the navigable River Wey, one mile from Guildford.' Obviously the new lease was not taken up, for in 1850 it was again advertised for sale.

The lease was then taken by H. Sanders, who continued until 1855, from which date the mill was taken over by Frederick & Henry Bowyer, in whose family it remained until 1938. It appears that the mill was in the sole occupation of Frederick Bowyer in 1862 until he met his untimely death from 'sunstroke' while riding over Woking Heath in July 1877. In 1887 the mill was again run as a partnership with a Mr Newell, and this arrangement continued until 1907, following which the occupiers were Bowyer & Son.

The extant mill building was erected in 1879 and can be regarded as of typical Victorian industrial design built to six storeys in red brickwork, although the window arches contain yellow brickwork in a futile attempt to add character to this ugly building. In 1893/4 it was converted to a roller mill with the waterwheel eventually replaced by turbines in 1915.

The present mill does not stand on the site of the original flour mill and is in fact positioned south-west of the mill house on the opposite side of the River Wey. The original flour mill, adjacent to the millhouse, was constructed in the conventional brick and weatherboarding style, more in keeping with the rural location.

The mill kept working until 1956, after which it was used as a warehouse to store industrial chemicals and then it formed part of a boat yard. In 1988 the mill was sold to a property developer who has converted it to office accommodation. The mill house has also survived the years and reputably dates from 1650, although it was extended in the latter years of the 19th century.

TILFORD MILL *Tilford*
River Wey SU 869443 — Located adjacent to Sheephatch Lane.

This is certainly an ancient mill site, as there is a reference to a fulling mill, used by Robert Graveshot in 1367. The site is to the north-east of the village of Tilford, in an area still named on modern Ordnance Survey maps as 'Tilfordmill', even though the mill bearing its name was demolished in the 1850s.

Corn milling was introduced by 1679, when it was marked on John Seller's map as 'Wanford Mill', while on other contemporary maps the site is shown as 'Tilford Mill'. The corn mill continued until at least 1850, but in 1866, a reference to an otter being trapped at the site of 'the old Tilford Mill', suggests the mill had been demolished. Thomas Piper was the last miller.

Today the position of the former watermill can be identified by an old brick residence known as Tilford Mill Cottage, part of which formed part of the old miller's house. This building lies next to the millstream, which diverges from the main body of the River Wey just below the site of Waverley Abbey. The mill stood by the weir, and some stone rubble, now half buried in the grass, may have been part of it.   87

UNSTEAD MILL *Peasmarsh*
River Wey Navigation SU 991460 — Located at the end of Mill Lane

This watermill was on the western bank of the Wey Navigation, next to Unstead Lock, and has been all but forgotten. No evidence of the large roller mill has survived, and it is difficult to visualise the massive bulk of such a mill, apparent to anybody using the Navigation towards the end of the 19th century.

The Ordnance Survey 6″ to 1 mile map of the area shows a 'Flock Mill' in 1913; what buildings that remained were pulled down soon after. The rubble was used to fill in the mill leat.

From 1832 until 1915 no less than seven tenants or partnerships were recorded. 1832–George Holland, 1834–Edward Chitty, 1845–Henry Moline, 1874–Richard and William Sisley, 1882–Sisley and Sholl, 1890–Francis Ashby. From 1903-05, Haikorn Ltd used the mill, but in 1906 it was advertised for sale, and corn milling ceased with the sale of the roller plant later that year.

The last buildings on this site were demolished in the 1950s, and part of the area is now used as a storage yard.

WAVERLEY MILL *Waverley*
River Wey SU 871455 — Situated adjacent to Waverley Lane.

To all intents and purposes the area known as Waverley was never more than a few cottages on the Farnham–Elstead road. Pasture land here became the site of the first Cistercian monastery in England, nearly 900 years ago, and such establishments always utilised a watermill. The site that was chosen was used over the following centuries by several mill buildings, the last of which ceased grinding in the final years of the 19th century.

In 1825 the mill was in the tenancy of Richard Varndell and stayed in the same family until its closure. It was still working in 1895, but was damaged by fire and finally demolished in 1900. The small brick and stone building which survives was erected to house electricity transformers, powered by a water turbine, still *in situ*, although the vertical shaft has been removed.

Next to the power house is the mill house, now renamed Mill Cottage, which is an attractive building of some antiquity. Beside the river, opposite the mill site, are the remains of an old sluice gate, constructed in ancient elm boarding, once operated by chains and levers.

WESTBROOK MILL *Godalming*
River Wey SU 966442 — West of Borough Road.

The site of Westbrook Mill formed part of an extensive layout of factory buildings, utilised over the centuries for a variety of trades, all of them obtaining power from the River Wey, which passes through the site. An examination of the Ordnance Survey 6″ to 1 mile map revised in 1913, illustrates the extent of the site, which at that time was producing leather products. This industry ceased in 1953, and the various outbuildings were taken over by the British Drug Houses. The whole range of factory buildings were demolished in December 1980 and, apart from the open concrete channel, nothing now survives to indicate the former industrial importance of this site.

At various times corn milling, paper-making, leather-dressing and fulling have taken place here.

The first reference to a leather mill was in November 1788, when a fulling mill was let along with a leather mill on the same site. The tenants of the leather mill were Messrs Denyer & Young; individual tenants involved included 1839, Fred Madely and 1851, Dalton & Madeley.

The latter had left by 1875, and the premises were up for sale, by auction, in June of that year. The leather mill was purchased by Messrs R. & J. Pullman, together with a corn mill on the site, but the leather mill was destroyed by fire in 1887. The whole group was completely gutted but rebuilding took place soon after and the same firm continued until 1953.

Originally the site was created for fulling mills — as far back as 1441. Towards the end of the 18th century the fulling mills were in decline, as flannel and linen manufacturing took over. In 1839, a trade directory described that 'The woollen trade had once flourished here, but has since disappeared'. The linen trade ceased in the middle of the century leaving only corn milling and leather-dressing on the site.

George Savage was the tenant of the corn mill here in 1862, but more detailed information appeared in the sale notice of Dalton's and Madeley's interest in 1875. The corn mill was known as 'Salgasson Mill' and contained four pairs of stones driven by a breastshot waterwheel 15ft 6in in diameter. No references to corn milling exist after this date, and the buildings were no doubt taken over for leather-dressing.

The site contained a paper mill, confirmed by a newspaper report of a fire in the leather mill in 1810 but, as the principal paper-making industry was centred at Catteshall Mill, the mill at Westbrook was no doubt closed down soon after.

WEYDON MILL *Farnham*
River Wey SU 836462 — At the end of Red Lion Lane.

Weydon Mill was almost certainly one of the six mills in the parish of Farnham documented in 1086, and in its early days it appeared in the Bishop of Winchester's Pipe Rolls of 1258.

In 1653 the mill was occupied by the Vernon family, and was said to contain '3 watermills under 1 roof', but this in fact referred to millstones. The last mill was established here in the 18th century to the south west of the town centre. It was a picturesque building with an undershot waterwheel driving four pairs of stones.

George Simmonds was the owner of Weydon Mill by 1834 and it remained in the family until 1892 with William Simmonds in occupation although, because of ill health, he employed William Smith to run it for him. Sydney Huggins was the miller until closure in 1909; in 1912 it was in such a poor state that attempts were made by local people to save and preserve it. However, the owner, William Trimmer, a local brewer, did not share their view, and in June 1919 he demolished it. The small and attractive mill house survived until 1957, at which time it suffered the same fate.

WILLEY MILL *Farnham*
River Wey (North Branch) SU 817451 — Adjacent to the Alton Road.

Willey Mill is the most westerly of the watermill sites in Farnham, being just half a mile from the county boundary with Hampshire.

A mill has stood here from Norman times and it belonged to the Bishop of Winchester from at least 1207. The existing Willey Mill building dates from the 18th century and is across the northern branch of the free-flowing River Wey, next to the Alton Road.

During the 18th and early part of the 19th centuries Willey Mill was associated with Bourne Mill, Farnham, but for no obvious reason since the mills were at opposite ends of the town. This was well documented in 1776 on the death of John Matchwick of Bourne Mill:

'Thomas Matchwick of Guildford and William Moon of Tilford, trustees of the late John Matchwick of Bourne Mill and Willey Mill, were granted the leases of three watermills, Bourne Mill, Bourne Malt Mill and Willey Mill. The Bishop of Winchester reserves the fishing rights.'

Daniel Arundell was the tenant miller and later in 1790, he is recorded as receiving a new lease from Matchwick's trustees. The Simmonds family took over in 1801 with William

Simmonds as the first miller, while he in turn passed it on to George Simmonds, who finally transferred it to John Simmonds, who stayed until 1878. Subsequent millers were 1878–William Carr, 1887–Henry Carr, 1895–Thomas Hall. Thomas Hall stayed until 1918.

The actual working portion of Willey Mill forms the central part of the existing buildings, and the abundant supply of water facilitated an undershot waterwheel. It was 11ft in diameter by 8ft 6in wide, but unfortunately removed for scrap in 1957. The pit machinery has survived and it follows the standard layout. The iron pit wheel is 8ft in diameter, with an all-iron wallower 3ft in diameter, while above is a 7ft diameter wooden spur wheel. The upright shaft is of pine and typically massive, 15in in diameter.

Willey Mill ceased trading commercially in 1953 and for the following four years the waterwheel powered a chaff cutter, oat roller and a crushing machine, all used for the manufacture of cattle cake. In July 1952 one ton of wheat was ground through one pair of millstones in eight hours. Apparently, the miller said that if the stones had been newly dressed the same task would have taken only five!

After the complete closure of the mill in 1957 the buildings, including the mill, were fully modernised and restored. The existing mixture of building styles, from different periods, gives the whole site an attractive appearance, especially the prominent half-hipped tiled roof of the mill itself. The pit machinery is rather dilapidated now, but it is still in reasonable condition. The wooden upright shaft, crown wheel and a boxed pair of millstones have also been retained, even though they appear rather out of place in their new and unconventional surroundings.

Until 1982 the whole complex was run as an antiques salesroom, but ownership has now changed and the outbuildings are used in connection with a trout farm.

WONERSH MILL *Wonersh*
Tributary to River Wey TQ 023446 — North-east of Norley Road

Wonersh Mill is an interesting building separated from the mill house by a large and typically idyllic millpond. The mill house dates from the 15th century but it has been comprehensively altered and extended.

There are two accesses to the mill, one by a public footpath from the south, and the other by way of a track that branches off the Guildford–Horsham road, which passes the mill house before leading up to the front door of the mill. Constructed in the side of the large pond embankment, the layout of the mill is conventional in that the raised entrance is straight onto the stone floor. The access to the pit floor is at the rear of the mill.

At first glance, Wonersh Mill appears of mid-19th century date, but a close inspection of the brickwork and especially the roof construction puts it a century earlier. The mill is built in the conventional style of brick to the first floor with tarred weatherboarding above. Loading and unloading was by way of a hinged door, as the front of the mill is only two storeys high and consequently there was no need for an elaborate lucomb.

The first documented reference to a mill appears on Seller's map published in 1679, when the site is marked as a corn mill. During the 19th century the corn mill was driven by an overshot cast-iron waterwheel, in turn replaced by a turbine in 1885, according to a sale notice on behalf of Lord Grantley, the owner:

'For sale, 15ft overshot iron waterwheel that cost about £130 some five years ago, priced £25. Also shafting, a good iron spur wheel, crown wheel, and wallower all in good order, priced £12'.

The modernisation of the mill was certainly completed by 1886:

'To be let, Wonersh Park water corn mill, Surrey. Recently fitted with new and most improved machinery.'

This 'new machinery' was not the usual roller mill system, but a simple layshaft driven by a turbine and working three pairs of peak stones, 48in in diameter, a pair of which remains intact, while only the bedstones remain of the other two. This layshaft system is complete and, although the turbine and primary drive shaft have been removed in connection with a survey of the mill in 1984, both pieces of machinery have been deposited by the side of the turbine pit. Although this system was installed over one hundred years ago it is in suprisingly good condition and, if the turbine was reconnected, it would surely work again without much attention. The owner of the mill has no immediate plans to modernise the building and, as this is one of only two remaining layshaft systems left in Surrey, and the most complete, it is important that it remains *in situ*.

Wonersh Mill ceased working in 1910 and is now used as a store room.

OTHER WEST SURREY WATERMILL SITES

Barford Lower Mill (SU 853380)
This was the largest of the three watermills at Barford, and was a paper mill until about 1850, after which it became a flock mill until its closure in 1884. Only the attractive mill house remains.

Barford Upper Mill (SU 854375)
This was a paper mill that worked in conjunction with the Lower Mill. Paper-making ceased here in 1830 and, apart from the large millpond, no traces remain.

Pitfold Mill (SU 881326)
One of the two watermills in Haslemere wholly within Surrey, this was a paper-bleaching mill before it was converted to a leather mill by 1871. The site ended its working life as a timber mill, using its own narrow-gauge railway.

There was also a silk mill north of Thursley (SU 919 409). Two ponds are situated just to the west of the A3, and between them stood a silk mill. In 1790, Lindley & Crosley marked it as 'iron mills' but in 1794 Thomas Nalder was recorded as insuring his silk mill here. The Tithe Apportionment Map of 1849 has Henry Pope as the occupier, who was also at the nearby Cosford Mill. The mill had gone by 1871.

91   Willey Mill in 1902 set across the River Wey. (JS)

OPPOSITE ABOVE: Sickle Mill at the turn of the century, when it was used to manufacture military braid. (JS) BELOW: The rear view in 1955; the pond has since been drained and filled in. ABOVE: The New Mill Shottermill lies derelict in 1909; BELOW: Shottermill after installation of the new machinery. (JS)

94

ABOVE: The large and extensive timber yard at Pitfold Mill. (SLSL)
BELOW: Bourne Mill, showing its irregular construction. (SPD)

ABOVE: The attractive Weydon Mill, tragically demolished in 1919. (CS) CENTRE: Farnham Hatch Mill was of a size appropriate to the importance of the town. (FF) BELOW: High Mill in 1900 when it ceased grinding commercially. (JS)

ABOVE: A view looking down Mill Lane to Godalming Hatch Mill. The mill ceased working in 1950. (SLSL) OPPOSITE LEFT: Godalming Hatch Mill situated in the centre of the town. Part of the front of the mill is supported on piles. (NC) RIGHT: Rack and pinion sluice controls at Westbrook Mill. (SLSL) BELOW: Salgasson Mill in about 1875 was a leather mill. (SLSL)

ABOVE: A leather mill at Godalming in 1840. BELOW: A traditional scene at Ockford Mill about 1907. (SLSL) OPPOSITE ABOVE: Eashing Mill was a paper mill and this engraving of 1840 shows three waterwheels. BELOW: Frensham Mill was demolished in 1922. (JS)

ABOVE: Enton Mill shortly before its closure in 1899. (JS) BELOW:
Barford Middle Mill, in 1909, was the only corn mill out of three at
Churt. (SLSL)

ABOVE: Barford Middle Mill in 1895 — note the wooden pole, seemingly holding up the side of the mill. (SLSL) BELOW: Snowdenham Mill in October 1939. The front is now virtually obscured by vegetation. (RCHME)

ABOVE: Bramley Mill was converted into a house about 1935. (SPD)
LEFT: Elstead Mill ceased working in 1878. (MH) RIGHT: The River
Wey passing under Elstead Mill. Note the wooden building sagging over
the river.

ABOVE: Wonersh Mill with the 15th century mill house in the background. (JS) BELOW: Dunsfold Mill in 1902.

LEFT: Cosford Mill in 1959 with the 15th century mill cottage sandwiched between the mill and the enlarged miller's accommodation. RIGHT: The ancient pit floor machinery at Cosford Mill. BELOW: Guildford Mill in 1986. It has become the scenery workshops for the adjacent Yvonne Arnaud Theatre. (NC)

ABOVE: Stoke Mill was erected in 1879 in typical Victorian fashion. It has recently been converted into office accommodation. (DK) LEFT: Abinger Mill, lying derelict in 1898. (SLSL) RIGHT: Wooden machinery at Rickford Mill in 1966. (SPD)

ABOVE: Pirbright Mill, with the doorway to the waterwheel clearly visible. BELOW: A view of Heath Mill across the millpond in 1904. (JS)

The miller, James Bailey, and his staff at Heath Mill. The once common
horse and cart have been replaced by more modern transport.

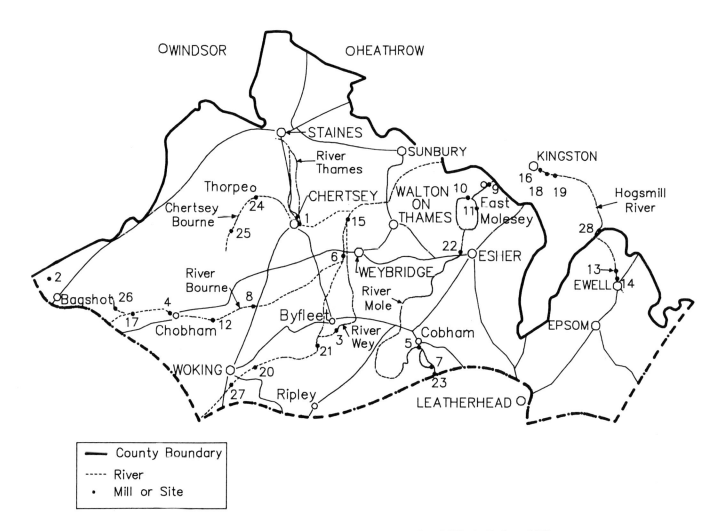

NORTH SURREY: 1. Abbey Mill, 2. Bagshot Mill, 3. Byfleet Mill, 4. Chobham, 5. Cobham Mill, 6. Coxes Lock Mill, 7. Downside Mill, 8. Durnford Mill, 9. East Molesey Mill, 10. East Molesey Upper Mill, 11. Ember Mill, 12. Emmett's Mill, 13. Ewell Lower Mill, 14. Ewell Upper Mill, 15. Ham Haw Mill, 16. Hog's Mill, 17. Hook Mill, 18. Kingston Middle Mill, 19. Leatherhead Mill, 20. Newark Mill, 21. Ockham Mill, 22. Royal Mills, 23. Slyfield Mill, 24. Thorpe Mill, 25. Trumps Mill, 26. Windlesham Mill, 27. Woking Mill, 28. Worcester Park Mill.

THE MILLS OF NORTH SURREY

ABBEY MILL *Chertsey*

Abbey River TQ 051671 — Track leading off Bridge Road east of town centre.

The Abbey at Chertsey was founded between 666–675, but it is doubtful whether a watermill was in existence here at the time. There is a reference to a Gilbert Fitzhalph in control of a watermill belonging to the Abbey in 1197, and a succession of mills occupied this site until 1899.

The mill was known in its early days as 'Oxlake Mill', and perhaps the first English illustration of an actual watermill appeared in 1432 on the plan of the demesne lands of the Benedictine Abbey at Chertsey. In the centre of the plan are two undershot watermills on opposite sides of a small river. This small river was created for the mills at this site, having been diverted from the River Thames at Penton Hook, then passing to the north of Chertsey and joining the Thames just to the north of Chertsey Bridge.

By 1700 the newly erected mills were flourishing and were in the ownership of Sir Nicholas Wayte and, towards the end of the century, a Mr Blake had taken control, with David Ireland as his tenant. Ireland insured the mills in 1778 for £200 which gives a fair indication that this was a large mill complex even then.

The La Coste family were in residence from 1805 until 1877, and they enlarged the mill considerably when they took over, primarily to accommodate the business gained from the three large undershot waterwheels fitted by them, together with bread ovens large enough to feed the inhabitants of Chertsey.

The mill complex was put up for sale in April 1877 owing to the death of Thomas La Coste, his brother George having died earlier. The sale notice stated:

'To be sold by auction at the Mart, London, by the instruction of the late T.B. La Coste. A very valuable freehold estate known as the Abbey Mills, with an unlimited water supply. Together with 88 acres of arable land, meadows and fishing rights.'

The list of fixed machinery included seven pairs of stones, driven by three internally mounted undershot waterwheels, two 16ft in diameter, and one 14ft in diameter.

At the auction, the mill and the surrounding meadow land were bought by Nathaniel Cook from Birkenhead, for £10,800. Cook only used the mill for a relatively short time and the site was again advertised for sale in 1899. The sale notice indicated the end of the mill and that the whole lot was 'taken down and lies conveniently for removal on the banks of the River Thames'.

A house now occupies the former site and the small river that provided water power for a thousand years now flows unchecked and without purpose.

BAGSHOT MILL *Bagshot*
Hale Bourne TQ 907631 — Adjacent to Church Road.

It is not often that a watermill is found at the top of a hill, but this unusual situation exists at Bagshot. There is no evidence to suggest that this is an ancient mill site. It is not even shown on the Ordnance Survey map published in 1816 although curiously, the millpond is. The reason for this is explained in Manning & Bray Vol 3 (1814), as follows:

'In the lower part of Bagshot is a watermill, supplied by pipes from a reservoir formed on the heath, on rising ground, about ¼ miles on the west. Mr Knight, who was a brewer, has quitted that business, and changed his buildings into a mill. The fall from the reservoir is about 48ft; the water is conveyed to the lower part of the building, from whence its rises to its level through a pipe fixed to the side of it, and is received in a system, from which it falls about 6' onto the wheel.'

Obviously this mill did not last very long, probably due to the rather complicated water supply system, and the existing mill building was erected nearer the reservoir. The mill displays a plaque dated 1817, with the initials 'CB', and this evidently is the date it was erected. Behind the mill is the reservoir, which was formed by the damming of a small stream that issues nearby, but overall, this is not one of Surrey's most picturesque mills. It was built of three floors of brick under a tiled roof, hipped back near its apex. Adjoining the mill is the mill house, with its more modern windows the only external difference between the two buildings. William Wright, a miller and brick maker, was made bankrupt here in 1818; George Spandwick was the miller in 1832 and remained until 1845, when G. Usher took over. In 1851 the mill contained two pairs of stones working on average, six to eight hours per day. Consequently, its flour output of twenty-five sacks per week made it the lowest producer of flour of the thirty-five mills recorded in the Water Resources Survey. In 1874 steam power was introduced with John Rice described as a 'Saw and Corn Miller at Bagshot Mill'. It is evident that the two trades continued together for some years.

The mill is shown on the Ordnance Survey 1/2500 map in 1894 as in work, but later in 1912 the Survey records it as a sawmill.

Of solid construction, it is inevitable that the building has survived. It is used today as a builders' store and no machinery remains. A survey of the mill in 1948 revealed that the waterwheel had been removed, but it was said to be over 24ft in diameter.

BYFLEET MILL *Byfleet*
River Wey TQ 072607 — At the end of a private drive off Mill Lane.

Byfleet Mill is difficult to find as it lies well hidden within the private grounds of the 18th century mill house, well away from a public highway. It is in picturesque surroundings with a water supply from a pond in front of the mill. This pond was connected by a leat to the River Wey, which isolates the mill and mill house on an island. Its exterior appearance is to a standard design with brickwork up to the first floor and weatherboarding above under a tiled roof. It is difficult now to imagine that over the past 300 years this site has been used for iron and brass wire manufacture, paper-making and corn-milling.

There is reference in the Domesday Survey to a mill at 'Biflet' worth 5s, and later in 1284 a Geoffrey de Lucy held the mill, owned by Chertsey Abbey, at an annual rent of 12d. The next reference appears in the accounts of the manor in 1673, with the first mention of a paper mill but that only lasted until 1711. From 1775 until 1790 small iron artifacts were manufactured here by Jukes Coulson & Co.

The existing mill building dates from the early 19th century; the first miller Thomas Rhyde in 1808 insured his water corn mill. That contained two waterwheels side by side, working separate machinery, in a similar arrangement to that found at Cobham Mill. In the sale particulars of the Oatlands estate in August 1822 it was said to contain four pairs of stones.

James Holroyd took over the mill and it remained in the family for some time. There was a tragic accident in April 1890 when William Holroyd, the eldest son of George Holroyd, caught his foot in a revolving belt and was crushed to death. It may well be that this accident persuaded George Holroyd to vacate the mill, for in the same year the well-known firm of Hall & Davidson took control, and ran it in conjunction with their other concerns at Ewell.

Byfleet Mill ceased working in 1930 with both waterwheels removed for scrap and by 1948 the buildings were disused and devoid of machinery.

CHOBHAM MILL *Chobham*
Hale Bourne SU 973619 — North of Vicarage Road, west of the village.

The demise of neighbouring watermills led to this mill being extended in 1897; the Ordnance Survey reveals that it was the only working watermill in this part of Surrey at the time.

The site was established by Chertsey Abbey, when it was known as 'Hurst Mill'. The last mill, erected here in 1790, was built of brick under a tiled roof, similar in design to that of Bagshot Mill.

The Water Resources Survey of 1851 reported that the mill contained two pairs of stones and produced, on average, 55 sacks of flour per week. Fred Benham was the miller in 1878 and it remained in his family until its closure. When the mill was enlarged, the iron waterwheel was retained although, in the early years of the century, a 'Marshall' semi-portable oil engine was installed. The engine was later found to be unsatisfactory, and was removed in 1916. The faithful waterwheel, then over 120-years-old, continued to power the mill until 1932, when a Gilkes turbine was installed.

The mill stopped working in 1950, after which it remained derelict, devoid of machinery, until it was destroyed by fire in 1967; a modern bungalow now occupies the site.

COBHAM MILL *Cobham*
River Mole TQ 110598 — Adjacent to Mill Road.

The small building that stands by the road on the approach to Cobham from the south was once one of a pair working side by side, but the larger of the two mills was pulled down in 1953 to facilitate road widening.

While the Domesday Book refers to a mill at Cobham, its site is not determined and the earliest reference to a mill on the present site was in 1534, when Richard Sutton leased it from the Abbey of Chertsey for 40 years.

The estate, including the watermill, was purchased in 1708 by the Viscountess Lanesborough, and a land settlement dated 1754 refers to Cobham Mill as in the tenure of Benjamin Casseldine. Thomas Lucy was the miller in 1777, although he had unsuccessfully attempted to buy it. John Tupper took over before 1787, and it was during his tenancy that severe flooding of the River Mole caused some damage. Tupper released the mill to James Peto in 1803 and he is recorded as taking up the lease on the 'repaired mill'. James Peto died in 1816 and was replaced by James Thorpe, who remained until he was declared bankrupt in 1824.

The new, and smaller mill, was erected in 1822 and it would be natural to assume that both mills would be run together, but Daniel Dallen was recorded as occupying a steam mill here from 1859 until 1882, with Thomas Sweetlove taking over until 1903, while the Batchelor family were in occupation, as Mrs J. Batchelor was in control of a mill here from 1851, and later in 1882. The final occupier of both mills was the milling firm of Henry Moore & Son.

The mills were closed down commercially in the early 1920s when the existing tenants relinquished the lease, and by 1925 the buildings had been sold to Mr C.H. Coombe, the owner of Cobham Park. Both buildings were under threat of demolition, but various newspaper reports suggested they should be retained and form part of a riverside park.

The waterwheels have collapsed and lie in a heap in the partly flooded wheelpit. These worked side by side and were both approximately 14ft in diameter, with the width of the smaller wheel 3ft 8in and the larger 10ft 6in. The tapered iron axle shaft that drives the smaller wheel now protrudes rather precariously through the flank wall and seems destined to follow the fate of the waterwheels and end up on the wheelpit floor. Inside the mill building, most of the machinery remains and, together with a pair of millstones, it is all contained on the pit floor. The iron pit wheel, 9ft 8in in diameter, meshes with a vertically mounted iron wallower, 3ft in diameter, that drives in turn an iron spur wheel 5ft in diameter. There is no upright shaft and all the machinery operates on a horizontal layshaft plane. The drive machinery is covered by a simple wooden hurst frame and set upon it is a pair of millstones, 4ft in diameter, bearing the manufacturer's plate 'Barron & Son, Gloucester'.

In recent years the future of the mill has been in some doubt and, as the River Mole here is prone to flooding, the Thames Water Authority were forced to implement regrading and bank repairs. Initially, there were no plans to repair or restore the mill, but the Authority and the Cobham Preservation Group between them have decided that it should be restored. The cost of the necessary repairs to both building and machinery will have to be met by the Group and work should start soon once a lease has been finalised with the Authority.

There seems no problem in re-erecting at least one of the waterwheels and getting it turning again, but it is unlikely that the building could support working machinery for structural reasons.

COXES LOCK MILL *Addlestone*
River Wey Navigation TQ 061641 — At the end of Downside Road.

Until 1983 Coxes Lock Mill was producing flour under the control of Allied Mills and, in its latter working days, electricity was used to power the 'Turner' roller milling system installed in 1934.

When the canal's company agent wrote a comprehensive report on the Navigation he made no reference to a mill at Coxes Lock. Construction started in 1776 and was not without problems, as an unknown consortium of businessmen decided that a leat should be excavated through the canal bank. The canal company at first refused permission for the excavation but in April 1777 the businessmen became impatient and instructed their employees to cut the padlocks on the sluice gates and put the mill in operation. The canal company eventually relented and allowed their water to be used, in return for the appropriate payment. By the summer of 1777 the difficulties had been overcome and Coxes Lock was working commercially with the full permission of the canal company.

In July 1782, Alexander Raby reached an agreement with the canal company to cut further channels through the west bank of the Navigation, to power his iron mill. Later, in January 1783, he secured the site and erected an iron forge where he remained until 1807. Raby then relinquished his licence from the canal company to John Taylor, who was described as an iron merchant from London. Taylor only stayed for three years for, according to a conveyance dated 20 February 1810, the mill was leased to William Thompson and William Foreman, who were described as iron merchants. In 1819 the iron mill was in the occupation of John Bunn and Alexander Carruthers, Bunn having moved here from the nearby Ham Haw Mill.

By 1829 Bunn had relinquished the iron mill and the iron manufacturing industry at the site finished. Daniel Lambert, the freeholder owner, built a corn mill and converted part of the new building to silk production, leasing the business to Thomas Wood for 21 years in 1834. It was then that the eight acre millpond was excavated, fed by the Navigation. The millpond was only 24 in deep and, because of the steady flow of water from the canal, filled up quickly.

In 1878 Benjamin Lambert leased the corn mill to Lorenzo Dundas, and William Slade, formerly the miller at Pixham Mill at Dorking. Dundas knew absolutely nothing about corn milling and relied upon Slade to run the business, but he was reputedly an easy-going character, and the business failed in 1887.

During this period only one waterwheel was used, that was 15ft in diameter by 5ft wide, and it drove six pairs of stones. There was once a second wheel but this had been taken out of use in 1867. Henry Adams and Samuel Ferns of Messrs R. & H. Adams of Bristol were the major creditors, and travelled up to Weybridge to wind up the business. Instead they took up a lease, on behalf of their employers, and later in 1900 they acquired the freehold and immediately constructed a new mill between the existing one and the mill cottage.

The new building was of seven floors and included a massive grain silo; it used a roller mill system powered by a turbine, the waterwheel having been scrapped. In 1904 the firm was renamed 'The Coxes Lock Milling Co Ltd'.

Over the ensuing years, the mill was continually improved and in 1954 Allied Mills took over. Water transport was available since up to eight barges could lie alongside the grain silo without obstructing traffic on the canal. Up to 1962 over 15,000 tons of wheat had been conveyed by canal to the mill but, along with the decline of the London Docks, commercial canal traffic dwindled. In 1964 the bulk of imported wheat was delivered from the adjacent railway, using a siding constructed specially for the mill.

In April 1983 Coxes Lock Mill was finally closed down by the Allied Mills Group and sold to a property developer. The building of 1900 has been gutted and converted to flats, while the waste land surrounding the mill now accommodates mock Georgian houses. The original mill built in 1820 has been partly demolished and its future is uncertain.

DOWNSIDE MILL *Downside*
River Mole TQ 118583 — Part of the Cobham Park estate.

Downside Mill lies by the River Mole at a point where it divides into two separate waterways which flow from north to south. The mill site is at the head of the narrower western branch that flows through Cobham Park, before rejoining the main river just upstream from Cobham Mill.

The mill was owned by Chertsey Abbey, and in 1331 reference is made to annual payments by tenants grinding their corn. A later reference in 1565, twenty years after the dissolution of Chertsey Abbey, chronicles an agreement between Thomas a Down and Thomas Lyfield, when a corn mill was in use. By 1687, the premises supported a corn mill as well as a paper mill, both in the occupation of William Berrey. Seven years later, the paper-maker here was John Meers, and an agreement of 1720 states that Thomas Morris was tenant of the corn mill as well as the paper mill, previously occupied by John Garton.

In 1733 Mary Hillyer insured her new paper mill, which was in the occupation of Richard Hinton, but there is no reference to a corn mill. The new paper mill replaced an earlier structure burnt down in suspicious circumstances in the early months of 1733, with the damage estimated at £1,658 together with £200 worth of paper. The paper manufacturing industry ceased production in 1770, when occupier Joseph Hunt was made bankrupt.

The site was rented by the ironmasters, Messrs Raby & Mereton, who converted the former paper mill buildings for iron smelting. By 1781 the site included one iron mill and two forges, and manufactured small iron goods. After thirty years of iron smelting the site was up for sale.

Raby was responsible for carrying out improvements to the watercourses at the site, as in 1806, Hugh Smith of Stoke House leased adjoining land to him to supply more water power. After Raby's departure, no buyer could be found for the iron mills and the buildings were utilised for a short time as a flock mill. A Thomas Miller was recorded as a paper-maker in 1839 but the venture did not last. Some years after, the premises were dismanted and the buildings to be seen on site today were erected for corn and saw milling. On the 1871 Ordnance Survey map of the area, the site is labelled 'Downside Saw Mill', as by then saw milling was the principal industry.

Although the buildings are devoid of any internal machinery, the iron breastshot waterwheel, of 15ft 6in diameter by 6ft 7in wide (frame measurement only) exists, but it is now sadly devoid of any floats. The corn mill was contained in that part of the building at the rear of the waterwheel, which necessitated some unusual primary drive machinery. The remains of the waterwheel show that it was a powerful wheel, generating at least 25–30hp. Also in the wheelpit is a small iron overshot waterwheel, of 5ft diameter by 1ft 6in wide, which was fed by water through its pentrough, set through the wall of the concrete millpond embankment. The waterwheel apparently worked continuously, pumping water to the various buildings on the site.

The former mill buildings contain just one solitary layshaft and, although the waterwheel, external primary drive machinery and watercourses are well worth a visit, the site lies on strictly private property. As a reminder of its former iron-working days, large quantities of slag adorn this once important mill site.

DURNFORD MILL *Woking*
River Bourne TQ 017619 — Adjacent to Durnford Bridge, Guildford Road.

Durnford Mill stood next to the River Bourne which is formed from the confluence of the Hale Bourne and Grants Bourne just downstream.

A watercolour of the mill, by John Hassell in 1824, shows it to be brick-built under a tiled roof, with 'Gothic' style windows inset haphazardly. The building appears small, but even so, it contained three pairs of stones, powered by an external wooden waterwheel, on the southern flank wall.

As with the nearby Emmett's Mill, Durnford Mill was included in the sale of the Ottershaw estate in 1819, and was then occupied by John Howe for £140 per annum. During the 19th century there was a succession of millers with John Bartlett in 1824, followed by Charles Baker from 1851–1862; during his tenancy the site was a flour and saw mill. Thomas Taylor succeeded Baker and finally Edward Hilder took over from 1878–1887, from which time the mill probably ceased trading. The mill is not marked on the 1/2500 Ordnance Survey map revised in 1893 so dismantling must have taken place by then.

This is now a most disappointing site and, although there is the suggestion of an overgrown mill leat, nothing tangible remains.

EAST MOLESEY LOWER MILL *East Molesey*
River Mole TQ 153682 — South of Creek Road

Since early times, Molesey was divided into two manors, Molesey Matham and Molesey Prior, and each possessed its own watermill, the Upper and Lower Mills.

Under the Commonwealth, both mill sites were acquired by a gunpowder manufacturer called John Samyne, and he became the second largest supplier of gunpowder in the country. It was only after a fire and explosion at the Lower Mill in 1666 that gunpowder production ceased there, but the Upper Mill site continued until 1780. The Lower Mill was converted to corn milling but, by 1699, part of the site was being used for the production of milled lead. John Martin held the lease of the corn mill in 1720 after the cessation of the lead industry, and the mill continued in the tenancy of the same family until 1817. Following the termination of Martin's lease, the tenancy advertisement stated that the mill contained eight pairs of stones, driven by an overshot waterwheel.

The mill was offered to the manorial lords by the Crown and on 12 October 1820 the purchase was completed. As new owners of the freehold, Lord Hotham and Sir George Berkeley decided it needed modernising, and in 1822 they erected a new mill on four floors, with two undershot waterwheels, 17ft in diameter, and of a value of £3,000.

After a short stay by Nathaniel Cherry, the lease was taken over in 1822 by Thomas Andrews, who was only 23-years-old. By 1845, and possibly earlier, Andrews had expanded the business, undertaking the sawing of timber and the supply of slates. To accommodate this extra trade he erected an additional building adjacent to the mill and by 1851 employed 17 men and four boys. The firm was expanded when his son, Herbert, and his son-in-law, Walker Garland, entered the business. Thomas Andrews died in 1892 and his son carried on and, although flour milling had been discontinued in 1890, the timber trade flourished. Herbert Andrews died in 1913, but the saw mill had closed down by 1905.

The mill stood unoccupied for some time and eventually a lease was arranged with the Zenith Motor Co, to manufacture motor cycles, in 1913. The company stayed there until 1930, when the business was wound up. The land surrounding the mill was purchased by Mr C. Nielson and Son, who founded a tent-making business in the old saw mill. In 1938 the buildings were taken over for the production of tools used in the manufacture of Bristol Blenheim bombers.

The two mill buildings were constructed in contrasting styles, with the saw mill built in a practical, but most unattractive fashion, with its prominent casement windows and overall typically Victorian aspect. The flour mill, on the other hand, was built of a yellowish brick, and altogether of a most pleasing appearance. The construction of both mills obviously attracted commercial use, but the former saw mill has recently been demolished along with all the other smaller buildings on the site.

The former flour mill has been taken over by an advertising agency, but the land surrounding the mill is shortly to be redeveloped for residential use.

EAST MOLESEY UPPER MILL *East Molesey*
River Mole TQ 144676 — South of Molesey Park Road.

Though there were originally two watermills on the River Mole at East Molesey, all traces of the Upper Mill have long since disappeared. The mill belonged to the manor of Molesey Matham and appears to have been solely a corn mill until the middle of the 17th century.

A lease was acquired on the mill site in about 1653 by John Samyne, for the purpose of manufacturing gunpowder. In 1666, a petition was sent to the King requesting the removal of both gunpowder mills as they had caused local residents to let or sell their homes and move away. Eventually, the petition was referred by the King to the Ordnance Commission, but nothing seems to have been done as Samyne was still at the site several years later. In 1669, a large explosion at the Upper Mill resulted in Samyne losing £1,200 worth of his own gunpowder and, more important, £600 belonging to the King, for which Samyne was responsible. This led to Samyne relinquishing his control at both mill sites, passing them both to his son, Peter. The site was later taken over by James Clarke, and he continued in occupation until 1730, when it passed to Robert Norman, and it was during his stay that a massive explosion took place on 26 October 1754 with loss of life. Upon the death of Robert Norman his son, James, took over the business, but he died five years later, control passing to Lord Hotham and Charles Sutton, and it was their decision to demolish the Upper Mill in 1780. Another explosion here in 1779 may have influenced that decision.

The waterways and various channels still remain at the site and now form part of a private sports ground.

EMBER MILL *Thames Ditton*
River Ember TQ 146671 — Situated north-west of Ember Lane.

The site at Thames Ditton was often worked in conjunction with Esher Mill, but it never did compete in terms of output with its more illustrious neighbour.

The first recorded industrial use of the site was as a corn mill, as mentioned in a survey of the manor of Imber Court in 1607.

In 1638 it was converted to the manufacture of brass wire under the direction of James Ledger. About 1649 the mill had been taken over by Jacob Momma and his partner, who were producing brass wire in greater quantities at the nearby Esher Mill. In 1672 the Imber Court estate was purchased by Shem Bridges and included a corn mill apparently in poor condition. Bridges was a lawyer and a considerable land owner in this part of Surrey. In 1693 he granted a lease to John Stapleton; under the terms of the agreement, Stapleton could rebuild the mill house and convert the existing buildings for the manufacture of brass and copper wire.

By 1705, following the death of Stapleton, a business partnership comprising Messrs Hitchcock, Wethered and Kent took over the lease, with John Hitchcock the leader of the group. It was decided to convert the existing buildings for the manufacture of iron hoops for barrels. Wethered, one of the original partners at the mill, was still manufacturing iron hoops here when he was described as the occupier of Ember Mill on renewal of the lease. Corn milling and iron fabrication continued side by side even when Alexander Raby took over from 1795 until 1802 but, after Raby's departure, the site reverted to corn milling.

In 1806 the lease for the corn mill was advertised and it was said to contain four pairs of stones and to be capable of grinding 40 loads of wheat per week from a 10ft head of water. The lease was taken up by Charles Sutton, who continued at the mill until 1812. An inventory of estate possessions made reference to a newly constructed watermill. The corn milling business was expanding, for there were two mills on opposite sides of the river. According to a report in a *Chelmsford Chronicle* of 1832, the watermill contained eight pairs of stones and was capable of producing 100 loads of flour per week and was one of a pair on the site. The advertised lease was never taken up and the mills were demolished, seemingly prematurely, soon after.

The exact position of the former mill buildings cannot be traced today, but the water channels constructed by Hitchcock in the early years of the 18th century still remain as a reminder of the industrial importance of the site.

EMMETT'S MILL *Chobham*
Hale Bourne SU 995618 — In Philpot Lane near its junction with Chertsey Road.

This is another mill site that was established on behalf of Chertsey Abbey. The existing mill building is of solid construction, in brick of three floors under a tiled roof, and was erected in 1701, but the attached mill house is earlier. The name of the mill originates from 1572 when Richard Emmett was in control.

The mill is marked on John Senex's map of 1729 and by 1783 Edward Jenkins was the miller. In 1819 the mill formed part of the Ottershaw estate and was advertised for sale. The sale particulars described it as having two pairs of stones with an attractive mill house, all in the occupation of John Lipscombe, at a rent of £200 per annum. At the time of the Water Resources Survey of 1851 James Mumford was the miller and the mill was producing forty sacks of flour per week with an annual turnover of £260, which was a reasonable return for a two pair mill. Robert White took over in 1874 and he was followed by Robert Taylor in 1887. Milling must have ceased soon after, for there are no references after 1900.

The frame of the waterwheel has survived and this is the only piece of machinery remaining from the eight watermills located in the Chobham/Chertsey area, a sad reflection. The waterwheel is constructed in three iron sections and is of the undershot variety, 10ft in diameter by 8ft 6in wide, and mounted on a 9in diameter circular wooden axle shaft. The machinery was removed when the mill was finally converted to residential accommodation.

Emmett's Mill is near a narrow unclassified road, and in front of the mill the Hale Bourne passes under an attractive humped-backed bridge, that has become a traffic hazard to the motor car.

EWELL LOWER MILL *Ewell*
Hogsmill River TQ 218629 — Adjacent to Kingston Road.

The last mill to occupy this site certainly would not win accolades for design. It was a large mill built almost entirely of brick, although it did have a two-storey wooden lucomb similar to that found at the Upper Mill.

The indications are that this was not an ancient mill site. The first known recorded occupier was William Jubb who, in 1732, insured the contents of his paper and corn mill all contained 'under one roof'. Paper-making was the principal industry. Jubb continued until at least 1794 according to a fire insurance entry, which again made reference to a corn mill. After Jubb's departure the timber mill building was replaced by a larger wooden flour mill. Thomas Sanders took over the new mill, having previously controlled the corn mill under Jubb's tenancy. By 1832, the milling firm of Hall & Davidson had taken control and continued until milling ceased in 1929. The same firm also had similar interests at Ewell Upper Mill from 1880, and Byfleet Mill from 1924.

A sale notice in June 1856 records that it was a three pair mill powered by an iron overshot waterwheel of 9ft 6in diameter by 8ft wide, and later, in 1891, a steam engine was installed by Messrs Crossly Bros to supplement the wheel. In 1896 the wooden mill was replaced by a much larger structure, which incorporated a roller milling system, driven by steam power, and this led to the miller, Jesse Ayling, leaving apparently in disgust. In a letter published in *The Times*, he complained most bitterly against the introduction of the roller milling system of milling wheat. Ayling certainly stood by his principles, for he left the Lower Mill shortly afterwards to take over the tenancy of Terwick Mill in Sussex.

After the mill ceased working in 1929 the building survived, albeit derelict, until it caught fire and was totally destroyed. The mill house, dating from the 17th century, survived the fire and is the only remaining feature of what was, in its time, a large and productive corn milling site.

EWELL UPPER MILL *Ewell*
Hogsmill River TQ 218629 — Adjacent to Kingston Road.

The site was certainly established here by medieval times and could well have been one of the mills listed in Ewell in the 1086 Domesday Survey. Close to the centre of Ewell, and lying west to Kingston Road, access to and from the mill was easy and convenient.

The mill is across the Hogsmill River at a point only 100 yards from its source, with two separate ponds between the mill and the point of issue.

It belonged to Chertsey Abbey, but the first documented reference appears on John Rocque's map published in 1768, when it is simply marked 'Corn Mill'. In terms of capacity the output of the Upper Mill was considerable as, from the mid-19th century, the mill contained six pairs of stones, although eventually a gas engine had to be installed to supplement the water supply. In its later working days only one pair of stones were used which, for such a large and spacious mill, was a sad reflection of the times.

The last mill to occupy the site was constructed in brick to the first floor with weatherboarding above, although there was more brickwork at the sides and rear. It is thought that that mill was erected in about 1810 and a sale notice, dated 22 January 1821 describes, what was then, a relatively new mill:

'Excellent and substantial water corn mill, beautiful lawns, gardens and orchard, fish pond, miller's cottage and pheasantry. Watermill with breastshot waterwheel driving 3-pairs of stones (french) and grinding more than 25 loads of wheat per week.'

The breastshot waterwheel was internally mounted with the tailwater bisecting the mill itself. The rather curious siting of the wheel tends to suggest that, before the major rebuilding in about 1810, the established water channel may have worked an outside waterwheel. The last breastshot waterwheel was made of iron, 20ft in diameter by 4ft 6in wide, to take full advantage of the limited water supply, and it was dated 1862.

The magnificent waterwheel, together with the internal machinery, was scrapped in the 1950s, when the Local Authority acquired the mill. Empty, the building served various purposes, with the Council finally converting it to offices, which included a caretaker's flat.

Prior to 1983 a visitor would have observed a white-painted weatherboarded watermill with a three-gabled frontage, along with an unusual lucomb spanning the two upper storeys. Following the decision to convert the building to office accommodation, assurances were made that the mill building would be tastefully restored. The same visitor returning to the site in the summer of 1984 would have had great difficulty in agreeing with such a statement, as the 'tasteful restoration programme' resulted in demolition of the majority of the mill building, so that at one stage just part of the rear wall and side wall remained.

HOG'S MILL *Kingston-upon-Thames*

Hogsmill River TQ 181688 — In Grove Road at the junction with Penrhyn Road.

This mill site is of ancient origin and was one of the five mills listed for Kingston in 1086. Even before then a 'water corn mill' was in the possession of Edward Standen in 1034.

For many years the mill belonged to Hounslow Priory until it was sold by the Crown in 1554. In 1633 it belonged to John Chapman, while later in 1767 Thomas Reynold insured his dwelling house and water corn mill, brick and timber, in the tenure of William Stevens. In 1781 the mill was in the ownership of William Scott with the same millier in occupation as in 1767. Five years later the tenancy had changed hands with Joseph Bickerton the miller.

It was at the beginning of the last century that the last of the watermills to occupy this site was built and it was a complete contrast to its predecessor. It was constructed on five floors under a slate roof, with a tall chimney added later for an engine. The mill was brick to the first floor with weatherboarding above and contained eight pairs of stones.

William Mercer took over the tenancy from William Stevens, and continued as miller until 1850, when it was known as 'New Mill'. The tenancy was transferred to Thomas Leonard, and finally in 1872 to the milling firm of J. & B. Marsh. The same firm was also using the steam-powered corn mill in Water Lane, just to the north of the town centre.

Even though Hog's Mill was a large and well-equipped watermill, the fierce competition from the port mills near the River Thames finally caused its closure in 1891. It was for sale in October 1891:

'A valuable freehold property situate in the centre of Kingston, comprising the "Kingston Corn Mill" and residence. It is a five floor flour mill with 8-pairs of stones driven by water power (breastshot wheel) and the auxiliary 16hp, steam engine with boiler house. To be sold with early possession. It has been for many years in the occupation of Messrs Marsh whose lease will expire at Lady Day next'.

Apparently the mill remained unsold and was reported in a derelict condition in 1895, when the owners advertised various pieces of machinery for sale. Hog's Mill was finally demolished in 1936 to make way for the Corporation Baths in Grove Road. Marsh's other milling concern, Down Hall Steam Mill, continued working until at least 1911.

HOOK MILL *Windlesham*
Hale Bourne SU 942620 — Adjacent to Burnt Pollard Road.

Along with its neighbour, Windlesham Mill, the site here was established on behalf of Chertsey Abbey in the early years of the 14th century. Unlike its neighbour, it survived for some time after and was certainly still working until at least 1895, when Hosea Humfrey was the miller. The mill appears to have been in the same family for some time as James Humfrey was the miller in 1832, and before him, Thomas Humfrey in 1812. In 1844 the miller was Daniel Inwood, while the mill itself was in the ownership of James Humfrey. By all accounts this was a fairly large mill, constructed throughout in timber, and clad in the traditional Surrey fashion of white painted weatherboarding under a tiled roof.

Regrettably this mill was demolished in 1899 and a modern house, ironically named Hook Mill, occupies the site. To the side of the house are the unmistakable remains of the millpond embankment, where the still plentiful Hale Bourne was dammed to channel the water to what must have been a breastshot waterwheel.

KINGSTON MIDDLE MILL *Kingston-upon-Thames*
Hogsmill River TQ 184687 — At the end of Mill Street

As the name of this mill suggests, this was the middle of the three watermills situated within a short distance of each other to the south-east of Kingston town centre. Undoubtedly it was originally a flour mill, but in its latter working years it was converted to make products derived from coconut fibre.

Middle Mill continued as a flour mill until 1848 when Joseph Cooper, a dealer in flour, was made bankrupt, after which corn milling ceased. In 1851 John Barsham & Co were recorded as Patent Cocoa Nut Fibre manufacturers and by 1862 the mill site had been taken over by the Patent Cocoa Nut Fibre Co. Over the ensuing twenty-five years the occupiers were Edward Hyde until 1866 and then W.R. Wilson & Co until 1878. By 1890, a printing works occupied the site and the buildings were considerably enlarged, thus ending the use of water power.

The mill site is about a quarter of a mile upstream from Hog's Mill at the end of Mill Street. The buildings, some of which no doubt date from the middle of the 19th century, are still divided by several water channels.

LEATHERHEAD MILL *Kingston-upon-Thames*
Hogsmill River TQ 187686 — East of Villiers Road.

There is no obvious reason for this ancient mill site to be known as Leatherhead Mill, since it is many miles from that town.

Until 1545 the mill and the surrounding land formed part of the Lovekyn's endowment of the St Mary Magdalene Chapel in Kingston until it was sold by the Crown. It is from its association with St Mary's that the site was called Chapel Mill and, along with the other two Kingston mills, Hog's Mill and Middle Mill, it was a corn mill according to the Tithe Account for 1535. In 1681 Richard Lant was the owner of both this site and Middle Mill, until he was succeeded by Elizabeth Stint in 1698. The site is marked as 'Leatherhead Mill' on Rocques map of 1768 but, by 1781, all references to corn milling had ceased.

On the cessation of flour production the mill site was converted to seed crushing, for in 1781 Stephen Wedge insured his oil mill, dwelling house, warehouses and utensils for £2,500. In 1809 a partnership between Thomas Stevens and Williams Stevens was dissolved with the lease advertised.

A succession of tenants then used the mill but, by 1878, oil production had ceased and the mill buildings lay derelict and empty until 1911, when they were used as a soap and candle works. The mill stood on an island channelled from the Hogsmill and utilised a breastshot wheel of approximately 16ft in diameter.

In the late 1940s the mill was demolished to make way for a council depôt, but there are still some old timber buildings, no doubt connected with linseed oil production. The mill house dates from the 18th century and was probably built when the oils mills were established here in 1781.

NEWARK MILL *Pyrford*
River Wey TQ 040574 — Adjacent to Newark Lane.

This was a massive watermill constructed entirely of wood, next to the River Wey Navigation. It is probably a Norman site as the 1086 Survey mentions one watermill. The mill took its name from the nearby Newark Priory, now in ruins, founded here in the 12th century and dissolved in 1538. Although there are a few vague references to the mill's association with the Priory, it is not until 1677 that Newark Mill is specifically recorded.

The Navigation provided ease of access to and from London and, along with Stoke and Coxe's Lock Mills, it probably ensured the mill's working life well into the present century. However, when barge traffic diminished, the financial viability of each site had to be reassessed and only Coxe's Lock Mill survived, until it closed down in 1983.

The oldest parts of the last mill to occupy the site date from the mid-17th century and, although additions were made in the next 200 years, it never lost its rustic appearance. The mill contained two waterwheels from an early date for, in a sale notice of 1795, part of the estate of Joseph Biddle included: 'Valuable corn mill at Newark with two waterwheels driving four pairs of stones, and capable of grinding over thirty loads per week.'

Edward Eager was the miller here in 1839 but Newark Mill was a paper mill between 1855 and 1859, probably in the occupation of Henry Brayley, who was also running a paper mill at Woking until his death in 1880. Newark Mill and its contents were offered for sale in September 1880 and included live and dead stock such as seven powerful cart horses, two useful cobs, cows, pigs, poultry, miller's wagon, carts, ploughs, harrows and a 14-ton open barge. Joseph Jarman had taken over as miller by 1895 and the business remained in his family until closure in 1943, after a bomb fell nearby and damaged part of the mill.

The two waterwheels referred to in 1795 were supplemented by a third wheel (external) in the 1850s. The two original wheels worked side by side in separate bearings inside the mill and were both 14ft in diameter, while the later wheel mainly worked ancillary machinery. Newark Mill contained eight pairs of stones although, towards the end of its working life, only half were capable of operation.

Some years after the closure the owners battled with the Woking Borough Council for permission to renovate the building and convert part of it to a restaurant, and to develop part of the site for housing; planning permission was refused. Alas, this delay led to the destruction of the mill, for in the early hours of a December morning in 1966 it caught fire. Within minutes the wooden mill was a blazing inferno despite the prompt attendance by the fire appliances from Woking and Guildford. Within an hour a building which had stood for over 300 years was reduced to a smouldering ruin. All that is left are the wheel pits and odd sections of brick footings, now set up as part of a landscaped garden.

OCKHAM MILL *Ripley*
River Wey TQ 056579 — At the end of a farm road, west of Portsmouth Road.

There are several early references to a mill at Ockham, the first in 1296 when it was noted that the manor of Ockham held two watermills valued at £2. On the Ockham estate map of 1706 two mills are shown on the same stream, one being the existing site, and the other about one third of a mile downstream. There are no records relating to the latter, although it is also marked on the small scale 'Ogilby' map of the same period.

The ownership of Ockham Park was conveyed to the Lovelace family during the reign of James I in the early 17th century. As part of the estate, Ockham Mill remained in the ownership of the same family until 1894, when William Lovelace died, aged 88. The existing mill dates from 1862, following the destruction of the previous one by fire.

The mill building is constructed in brick in the distinctive style favoured by the Lovelace family, with flat arched recessed windows and a sprinkling of cut brick string courses inlaid with terracotta tiles. At the side of the mill, adjacent to the farm track, is a substantial two-storey lucomb supported on cast-iron angle brackets. This is a fine example of a Victorian mill.

The waterwheel, mounted internally, is a superb example of a low breastshot wheel constructed in iron of 14ft 6in diameter and 9ft 10in wide with four sets of arms. It is set on an iron shaft which bears the legend 'Filmer and Mason, Engineers, Guildford. 1880'. This shaft must have been a late addition, as the pit machinery and waterwheel were installed when the mill was built. The drive machinery is also constructed in iron and is assembled in a standard layout to drive five pairs of stones. The iron pit wheel of 9ft 6in diameter drives an iron wallower, cast in two sections, with a diameter of 4ft 10in, and above this is an iron spur wheel of 10ft diameter. The mill was supplied by water taken off the River Wey some distance away by means of an artificial channel. This water supply then filled a millpond, which in turn was discharged back to the mill race by means of sluice controls. The water was then controlled directly onto the wheel by another sluice made up of sliding wooden boards but, even during the dry summer months, there was never a shortage of water.

The miller in 1862 was Henry Bowyer and he stayed for fifteen years. Alfred Tice took over and remained until 1899 after which the large agricultural firm of Henry Moore & Son took over. In 1927 the mill stopped work; it never worked again and the mill lay disused until 1958 when it was put up for auction as part of the Ockham Park estate. The building was then converted to a private house. Initially, the pit machinery was restored by the well-known Sussex millwrights, Messrs Hole & Sons, while a recent owner of the mill decided to get the fine waterwheel turning again. This was accomplished using professional millwrights and the wheel and pit wheel now turn regularly.

Although named Ockham Mill, the site lies some one and a half miles north-west from the village centre and, in fact, is nearer Ripley. The mill forms the centre of a group of red brick buildings which includes Millstream, the 18th century miller's cottage.

ROYAL MILLS *Esher*
River Mole TQ 131658 — At the end of Mill Lane.

The mill site at Esher has long been associated with such diverse industrial manufacturing processes as brass wire production, paper-making and corn milling.

The River Mole here, more often than not had a good supply of water and, by the artificial division of the main river, a leat was formed to channel the water to the site. It appears to have been used mainly for industrial processes and, although corn milling did take place, it was never on a large scale.

The history of the site during the medieval period is rather confused and unclear. Although a mill is often referred to in various land transactions, its type and usage is unknown. The first major manufacturing industry to occupy the Esher site commenced in about 1649 when Dutchmen Jacob Momma and Daniel Demetrius began producing brass wire, using rose copper imported from Sweden.

In 1691 Esher Mill was taken over by a company headed by William Dockwra, who continued to manufacture brass wire, but after such a flourishing beginning, things started to go dramatically wrong. In 1709 a merger was arranged with the Bristol Brass and Battery Company.

The union with the Bristol-based company ended in the 1740s, when ownership of the site passed to William Hughes, who in turn leased it to Joseph Biddle, a corn merchant and miller. Biddle converted part of the buildings to a corn mill but the site was still known as the 'Wire Mill' and it appeared as such on Rocque's map of Surrey published in 1768. The corn mill closed in 1795 when Joseph Biddle, a descendant, was declared bankrupt. For a short time after, the buildings went over to the production of iron hoops, for in 1798 Matthew Puplett insured his 'hoop mill' for £600.

Corn milling started again, and carried on until 1847, with Richard Batchelor the last miller.

In 1847, a substantial paper mill was erected but, after a fire in 1853, paper production was moved to Wandsworth. Attempts to manufacture gun cotton failed, and the site was used by the Esher Linoleum Co.

In the early 1900s it was purchased for £5,000 by the bookbinding firm of James Burn and, after another fire in 1908, electricity replaced the steam engines and undershot waterwheels. Owing to flooding problems, extensive river regrading and realignment has removed any traces of the mill leats and sluices.

SLYFIELD MILL *Stoke D'Abernon*
River Mole TQ 133578 — In the grounds of Slyfield House adjacent to Cobham Road.

The site of Slyfield Mill is near a country lane in an area unspoilt and unaltered for centuries — unspoilt, that is, until the Government decided that the M25 motorway should pass through this once quiet and tranquil part of Surrey.

This was certainly a Domesday mill site, by the River Mole, in the parish of Great Bookham at its boundary with Stoke-D'Abernon. The mill was positioned some fifty yards up a private drive that leads into the grounds of Slyfield House. From the middle of the 14th century at least, it was used as a fulling mill as well as a corn mill and much later, in 1614, it still carried out both trades.

The last mill that stood here was erected in the second half of the 18th century, and was constructed to a conventional style in brick and timber. In 1776 Henry Bray insured the contents of his brick and timber water corn mill for £250. Bray was still the occupier in 1808, while later in 1832 the miller was John Giles, but in 1846 the trustees who administered the Slyfield estate closed the mill down.

THORPE MILL *Thorpe*
The Bourne TQ 021679 — Situated adjacent to Mill Lane south of Thorpe.

This is an ancient mill site, near to Chertsey Abbey, probably under its control for many years. In 1784 John Finch was the miller, but nine years later, it was used by a Mr Bugbey for spinning thread.

In 1851 Mr Smyth was the miller, followed shortly after by William Gaylor. A partnership between Charles Brazier and William Boreham existed here in 1862 but, later in 1882, the former partner was the sole occupier. John Wiltshire was the last miller until closure at the turn of the century.

Thorpe Mill was built on three storeys of weatherboarding with a lucomb protruding from the bin floor, with the entry into the mill by a flight of steps leading up to the stone floor. The mill was attached on one side to a two-storey brick building, the miller's accommodation, and on the other side to a brick-built store.

The building was mainly used as a farm store until 1924, when it was purchased, repaired and opened as a restaurant in 1928. The framework of the waterwheel, 12ft in diameter, was all that remained of the mill machinery but, when the restaurant closed down in 1960, the mill building itself was doomed. Unfortunately, it lay in the centre line of the proposed M3 London--Basingstoke motorway. In April 1970 the mill was set alight by the road contractors and literally burnt to the ground.

TRUMPS MILL *Egham*
The Bourne TQ 005674 — Adjacent to Trumps Mill Lane.

Trumps Mill was a watermill tucked out of the way and reached by a narrow and winding road called Trumps Mill Lane. Before the M3 Motorway was constructed, this must have been an idyllic setting, but now, with that road only 200 yards south, the tranquillity of the area has been shattered.

There is a reference to this ancient mill site in 1299, while later in 1519 a watermill called 'Trumpes Mill' was granted with Milton Manor to the College of Corpus Christi. Tithes to the value of 21s 4d were paid to the almoner of Chertsey Abbey until the Dissolution.

Three millers prominent during the 19th century were Stephen Murrell, (and then his executors until 1880), James West until 1890 and finally H. Hedges until the closure of the mill in 1909. The mill was brick to the first floor with two floors of white weatherboarding above. The internal waterwheel was iron, 8ft in diameter by 4ft wide, driving four pairs of stones.

The mill was fed by a small, but consistent, supply of water from the Bourne but even so, an artificial embankment was constructed to pond the water at the back of the mill. The mill was attached to the mill house, which was extensively modernised in 1930.

WINDLESHAM MILL *Windlesham*
Hale Bourne SU 927629 — Located south-west of Hook Mill Lane, south of Windlesham.

This ancient mill site, along with its near neighbour, Hook Mill, belonged to Chertsey Abbey. As late as 1832 both this and Hook Mill were run together, with James Humfrey as the recorded occupier of both.

It was advertised for sale in 1831 and the sale particulars reported it was profitable. The Water Resources Survey of 1851 records that it was only a two pair mill, working on average only six hours per day and capable of producing, on average, 30 sacks of flour per week. The Survey also reported that the machinery was in poor condition and that the site was also used as a saw mill. The mill ceased working soon after 1851 and the site, adjacent to the M3 Motorway, is totally devoid of any remains.

WOKING MILL *Woking*

River Wey TQ 016564 — Situated west of Broadmead Road, Old Woking.

The Domesday Survey records one mill at Woking, but later, in the 14th century, the manor possessed a corn mill and a fulling mill. Later still, during the reign of Henry IV, a watermill was classified as 'weak and ruinous', of annual value 6s 8d, while the fulling mill was let at an annual rent of 8s.

In 1671 James Zouch, lord of the manor, leased both buildings as corn mills to James Collyer, while much later in 1749 a sale notice for the mills stated: 'To be sold pursuant to a decree of the High Court of Chancery, the great tithes of Woking Park, a farmhouse and land with two water corn mills and a water powered snuff mill with a dwelling house.'

At the end of the century, in 1796, the mills were again up for sale, as a notice stated: 'To be sold by auction at the White Hart Inn, in Guildford, on the 11th July 1796. All those capital freehold flour mills and a leather mill, called Wokeing Mills. The flour mill is in the occupation of Mr Ryde and the leather mills used by Mr Richard Baker. Together with the tolls, or duties called riverage for barges navigating the River Wey.'

The flour mills were on opposite sides of the river and were supplemented by an ancillary building that was a snuff mill in 1749, a leather mill in 1796 and a paper mill, occupied by Venables & Co, in 1832. A sale notice in May 1850 stated that recently erected paper mills were for sale, powered by two large waterwheels installed to drive the paper mill machinery. Henry Brayley was the paper-maker in 1851, while Mr J. Fladgate was the corn miller, but no mention of a corn mill can be found after this date. In 1894 the site was known as the 'Woking Paper Works Ltd', while two years later, Unwin Bros' printing works were the occupiers.

Today, the site is covered by large semi-modern brick buildings, none of which are associated with the former paper mill.

WORCESTER PARK MILL *Worcester Park*

Hogsmill River TQ 210658 — Adjacent to Old Malden Lane.

Both the gunpowder mill and the later corn mill were on a site attributed originally to Tolworth in the Domesday Survey.

In the middle of the 16th century, the manors of Tolworth and Thames Ditton were acquired by George Evelyn; by 1589 he held a number of patents for obtaining saltpetre and making gunpowder and he set up a mill here. He later moved to Godstone and started a powder mill at Leigh Mill. His son, Thomas, took over the running of the mill, along with other sites, and continued here at least until 1605. William Taylor had taken over by 1742, and it remained in the family for many years.

In 1771 the celebrated civil engineer, John Smeaton, installed an overshot waterwheel 9ft in diameter by 6ft wide. Smeaton, among other things, was at the time testing and developing the efficiency of various types of waterwheel, and the wheel installed here may have been to a 'new' design.

Worcester Park Powder Mills continued in operation under the control of Fred Taylor, until 1854, when a vast explosion wrecked the site. This marked the end of gunpowder production and later, in 1874, a corn mill was built with Jabez Hover as the miller. A sale notice of 1879 reveals that the mill contained four pairs of stones along with a newly erected eight-roomed house, but in 1891 the mill caught fire at a loss estimated at £2,000. After the fire, the buildings still standing were used for watercress growing and later for silk screen printing.

Over the years, there were other references to this site as 'Tolworth Mill', but the 1871 Ordnance Survey Map labels it quite clearly as Worcester Park Mill, and it is this name that is most commonly used.

A Victorian cottage, adjacent to the site, bears the name 'Old Mill Cottage' and in the front garden lies a large bedstone, a relic of its former gunpowder days, while behind the property are the unmistakeable remains of a tail race.

OTHER NORTH SURREY WATERMILL SITES

Ham Haw Mill (TQ 072654)
Adjacent to the River Wey Navigation this mill produced paper, iron and brass goods, flour, vegetable and linseed oil. It ended its days as a linseed oil mill, when damaged by fire in 1963.

Powder Mills (TQ 211636)
A large gunpowder production site on the Hogsmill River at Ewell, it was established here in 1720. At one time there were four waterwheels. The site is still evident by the number of water channels to be seen.

Byfleet Mill ceased working in 1939 and is now used for storage. (SPD)

ABOVE: From an architectural point of view, Downside Mill is an undistinguished mill building. (NC) BELOW: The framework of the low breastshot waterwheel there. (NC)

ABOVE: The Upper Mill at Ewell awaiting restoration. (NC) BELOW:
Ewell Lower Mill in 1873. (BHM)

A brick built roller mill replaced the wooden mill building at the Lower
Mill. (BHM)

LEFT: Although Hog's Mill ceased trading in 1891, it was not demolished until 1936. (KMHC) RIGHT: Emmett's Mill was erected in 1701; it now bears little resemblance to a mill. BELOW: The buildings of the former Leatherhead oil mill, adjacent to the Hogsmill River at Kingston-upon-Thames.

Thorpe Mill succumbed to the construction of the M3 Motorway in 1970.

ABOVE: The Abbey Mill at Chertsey had three internal waterwheels. (CM) BELOW: Bagshot Mill now bears little resemblance to its industrial past.

ABOVE: Little is known about Durnford Mill. (CM) BELOW: Newark Mill must have been Surrey's best known watermill, until it was destroyed by fire in 1966. OPPOSITE ABOVE: Ockham Mill was built in the distinctive style favoured by the Lovelace family. The photograph dates from about 1900. BELOW: The two watermills at Cobham: the larger mill was demolished in 1953 for road widening. (JS)

ABOVE: Woking paper mill was in a state of general decay at the turn of the century. BELOW: An aerial view of Coxes Lock Mill shows its ease of access to road, rail and canal transport.

The barge 'Perseverance' in front of Coxes Lock Mill in 1889. (WM)

ABOVE: The 'Turner' roller milling system in operation at Coxes Lock
Mill in 1979. BELOW: Ham Haw oil mill at the turn of the century. (JS)

Wonham Mill in 1895.

GLOSSARY

Ark — A bin for holding grain.

Axle — Shaft linking waterwheel with pit wheel.

Bedstone — The lower and fixed millstone.

Bin — Container for storing grain on the top floor of the mill.

Bit — Metal cutting tool used in stone dressing.

Bolter — Used for the dressing or sifting of flour.

Breastshot Waterwheel — Wheel where the water is projected against its centre. Variations are high or low.

Bridge Tree — Beam of the hursting that supports the lower end of the stone pivot.

Brigging — Process that ensures that the stone spindle is vertical.

Buckets — Fittings around the waterwheel that hold water.

Burr Stone — Millstone quarried near Paris.

Clasp Arm — Wheel whose spokes form a square around the shaft.

Compass Arm — Wheel whose spokes radiate from the shaft.

Cogs — Removable wooden teeth of a gear wheel.

Corn — Grain or seed of any cereal crop.

Corn Laws — Regulatory statute to control the import of foreign wheat.

Crook String — Used to regulate the opening from hopper to shoe.

Crown Wheel — Cog wheel at the top of the upright shaft; drives ancillary machinery.

Damsel — A device for jogging the shoe to regulate the flow of grain to the stones.

Dresser — Used for grading flour; wire or silk lined.

Dressing — Process of sharpening millstones when worn.

Elevator — Arrangement for carrying grain vertically.

Eye — The opening in the runner millstone through which grain enters.

Floats — The wooden or metal paddles on a waterwheel.

Grist — Animal feed ground at a mill.

Headrace — Section of stream above a mill, frequently referred to as a leat.

High Milling — Process involving the reduction of flour in several stages.

Hopper — Open topped wooden box through which grain passes to millstones below.

Hurst — Framework supporting millstones and enclosing pit gearing.

Jack Ring — Mechanism for disengaging stone nut.

Leat — see Headrace.

Low Milling — Process of producing flour by passing grain once through the millstones.

Lucomb — A cabin projecting from the bin floor containing hoisting gear.

Mill Bill — Implement used for stone dressing, consisting of a handle and bit.

Millstones — Two stones made of burr, peak or composition material.

Overshot Waterwheel — Water is projected past the top of the wheel.

Peak Stone — Millstone quarried in Derbyshire.

Pentrough — Trough conveying water to the waterwheel.

Pinion — Small type of gear wheel.

Pit Wheel — The first gear wheel inside mill, affixed to wheel axle shaft. Usually iron with wooden cogs.

Pond Bay — The dam or embankment of a millpond.

Race — Water channel above or below waterwheel.

Runner Stone — The upper millstone revolving over bedstone.

Sack Hoist — Used to raise flour or grain up and down through the mill.

Shoe — Tapering wooden trough leading from hopper to eye of millstone.

Sickle Dressing — Method of dressing millstones in a curved furrow radiating from centre.

Smutter — Ancillary machine for removing diseased particles of wheat.

Spur Wheel — Affixed to upright shaft, above the wallower, engaging the stone nuts.

Starts — Wood supporting floats on waterwheel.

Stone Nut — Pinions engaging the spur wheel; keyed to pivot on which runner stone is turned.

Stone — See Millstones.

Stone Spindle — Shaft attached to runner millstone.

Tentering — Process of controlling space between millstones.

Thrift — Wooden handle of mill bill.

Undershot Waterwheel — Water is projected under the wheel striking the paddles.

Upright Shaft — Vertical wooden or iron shaft.

Wallower — Small toothed gearwheel affixed to upright shaft and driven by pit wheel.

Wire Machine — See dresser.

*I*NDEX

BIBLIOGRAPHY

Bennet, R., and Elton, *History of Corn Milling* (4 Vols) Simpkin Marshall 1899

Brunskill, R.W., *The Illustrated Handbook of Vernacular Architecture* Faber & Faber 1972

Hillier, J., *Old Surrey Watermills* Skeffington & Sons 1951

Pevsner, Sir N., *The Buildings of England — Surrey* Penguin

Reynolds, J., *Windmills and Watermills* Hugh Evelyn 1970

Reid, K.C., *Watermills and the Landscape* SPAB 1959

Watermills of the London Countryside Charles Skilton Vol 1 — 1987, Vol 2 — 1989

Surrey County Council List of Antiquities and Conservation Areas 1976

Sutcliffe, J., *Instructions for Designing and Building a Corn Mill* 1816

Syson, L., *British Watermills* Batsford 1965

The Watermills of Britain Batsford 1980

Vince, J., *Discovering Watermills* Shire Publication 1987

Mills and Millwrighting Shire Publication 1978

Watts, M., *Corn Milling* Shire Publication 1983

Wilson, P.N., *Watermills, an Introduction* SPAB 1985

SUBSCRIBERS

Presentation Copies

1 Surrey County Council
2 Surrey County Library
3 Professor A.G. Crocker FSA DSc CEng
4 David Shepherd OBE FRSA

5 Derek and Moira Stidder
6 Tom Stidder
7 Barry Stidder
8 Amy Stidder
9 Clive and Carolyn Birch
10 Croydon Natural History & Scientific Society
11 Paul W. Sowan
12 S.D. Smith
13 Miss Lynette Rispoli
14 Gordon Button
15 Margaret Thompson
16 Anita Guy
17 Ron Burton
18 Geoffrey Morris
19 Roy F. Greasby
20 Mrs E. Franks
21 Martin Newton
22 Carol & Ken Dryden
23 K.R. Geddes
24 Mr & Mrs V.P. Marciandi
25 Donald Neville
26
27 Clara D. Stidder
28 Rosemary & Bill Locke
29 Alan Stidder
30 B.G. Bellingham
31 G. Wallis
32 Patricia Loarridge
33 Society for Protection of Ancient Buildings, Wind and Watermill Section
34 Donald S. Paterson
35 Send Court Farm
36 Mr & Mrs John Bennetts
37 C. Taylor
38 John Pelling
39 John Hayes
40 Michael H. Yates
41 Alan John Mitchell
42 Roy Henderson
43 Mrs P. Dick

44 E.B. Bugin
45 Robin V. Clarke
46 Keith Preston
47 Jim & Frances Bowles
48 Victor & Sandra Deschamps
49 Alan & Glenys Crocker
50 David C. Taylor
51 R.A. Lowe
52 Miss V.A. Luck
53 James Woodward Nutt
54 Nigel Moon
55 Tjerk Oosterhuis
56 Clyde Thomas Riley
57 D. Crook
58 Ronald John Fowler
59 D. Cole
60 A.R. Killick
61 Maurice A. Groves
62 S.E.D. Fortescue
63 Robin L. Marsh
64 P. Bailey
65 Mick Finnemore
66 R.W. Smith
67 Julian Pooley
68 P. White
69 Colin Armstrong Smith
70 John W. Hill
71 J. Day
72 Paul J. Baker
73 Barry Job
74 J. Kenneth Major
75 Michael Oakley
76 Michael Simpson
77 Mr & Mrs A.D. Dinkin
78 Catherine & Richard Darby
79 Aubrey E. Hide
80 J.W. Middlemas
81 M.H. Edgeworth
82 D.T.N. Booth
83 Derek Brown
84 David Odd
85 Mrs Margaret Lovelock
86 Mr & Mrs Parr
87 Dorking & District Museum

88 Peter Goodall
89 I.H. Liebert
90
91 W.N.T. Roberts
92 N.M. Catford
93 A.A.W. Budd
94 Mrs P. Brown
95
96 Miss Rita J. Ensing
97 Andrew Abbott
98 A.R. Heygate
99 A.R. Heygate (Junior)
100 Robert Sier
101 Alan Stoyel
102 Mr & Mrs R. Proctor
103 Jack Hillier
104 E.A. Crossland ISO
105 Michael Wilks
106 P.J. James
107 Mrs J.E. Duggan
108 A.F. Tullett
109 J.H. Sheppard
110 Anne & Les Bowerman
111 Jenny Pemberton
112 Egham Museum Trust
113 Edward Sammes
114 John A. Blair
115 Jean Shelly
116 David Knight
117
118 Michael Elphick
119 Mrs Jean West
120 Douglas F. Pluck
121 Crispin Hill
122 Sutton Central Library
123 W.G. Steer
124 Michael John Fuller
125
126 Nigel Melican
127 Nigel Coates
128 G.V. Hodges
129 June & Peter Francis
130 Susan M. Tombs
131 H.R. Darking
132 John D. Boas
133 Peter Hexton
134 Walter Buchanan
135 E.W. Henbery
136 Unlisted

137 Jo Roberts
138 Dr A.J. Ward-Smith
139 P.S. Jarvis
140 Mrs M.K. Brooks
141 Maralyn Anstiss
142 Farnham Museum
143 John B. Gent
144 A.B. Mann
145 N.T. Walder
146 Annamaria Radici
147 Gordon Knowles
148 M.C.A. Hookey
149 Geoffrey Holman
150 M.R. Pattinson
151 T.J. Martin
152 D.P. Van Beesten
153 Richard Faircliff
154 Daryl Fowler
155 R.J. Barnes
156 J.M. Adams
157 S.D. Robertson
158 Paul Dawson
159 John King
160 Jean Arnold
161 Roy & Sandra King
162 Kingston Heritage Centre
163 P.M. Pearce
164 Dr Jenny West
165 John Axten
166 D.J. Turner
167 Stephen Nelson
168 Dr G.P. Moss
169 Holmesdale Natural History Club
170 Nicholas Kelly
171
172 F.W. Gregory
173 John Wright
174 Bartley Mill
175 Robert Girling
176 David Barmes, EKMG Member
177 D. Leatherdale
178 John Ronald Sweetapple
179 Roger Matthews
180 J.D. Davies
181 Science Museum Library, South Kensington
182 J.W.F. Cannon
183 Anthony Harcombe
184 G.A.R. Illsley

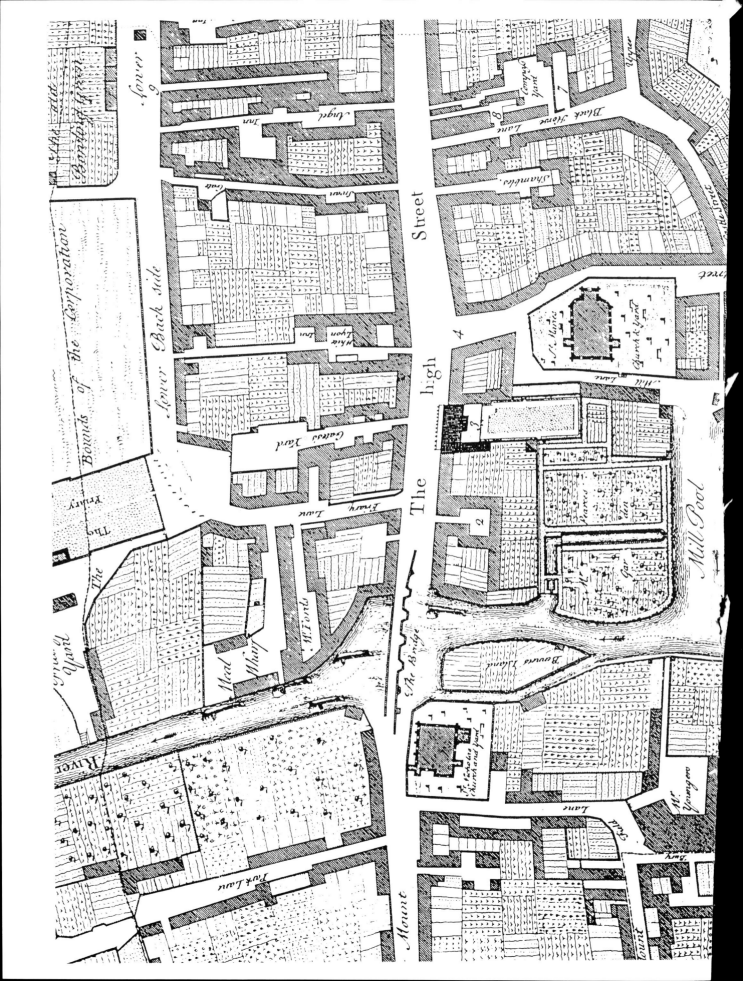